MW00575501

WHERE SILENCE ENDS

WHERE SILENCE ENDS

ANGELA RUIZ & MARY RUIZ

To my mom, dad, sister, brother, partner, tíos, tías, cousins, nieces and nephews (those to come), my kids who will one day come, extended family, and the world.

But mostly, to my mom.

She knows how to brighten up the world and she does it coming from the dark.

Dear readers,

As you go through this book,
If you're angry and you feel like ripping the page up, rip it.
If you feel like screaming, scream.
And if you feel like holding the book up close to your heart, hold it.

SPANISH / ENGLISH Index

Abuelita	Grandma
Abuelito	Grandpa
Abuelitos	Grandparents
Apa	A term for 'Dad'
Atole	Hot corn beverage usually mixed with cinnamon
Carnitas	Braised pork
Día de los Muertos	Day of the Dead, a Mexican holiday honoring those who have passed on
Mija/o	My child (pronounced mee-ha/ho)
Prima	Cousin
Reboso	Large shawl
Señora	Mrs.
Señor	Mr.
Tamales	Dough stuffed with variety of ingredients, steamed and wrapped in corn husk or banana leaf
Tía	Aunt
Tío	Uncle
Tortas de papa	Potato tortas
Quinceañera	Latin rite of passage celebrating a female turning 15, signifying her ascent into womanhood

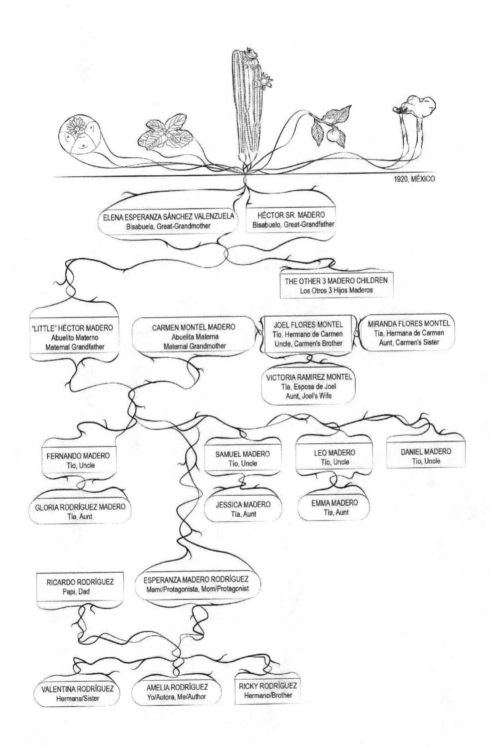

1920, MÉXICO

ELENA ESPERANZA SÁNCHEZ VALENZUELA
Bisabuela, Great-Grandmother

HÉCTOR SR. MADERO
Bisabuelo, Great-Grandfather

THE OTHER 3 MADERO CHILDREN
Los Otros 3 Hijos Maderos

"LITTLE" HÉCTOR MADERO
Abuelito Materno
Maternal Grandfather

CARMEN MONTEL MADERO
Abuelita Materna
Maternal Grandmother

JOEL FLORES MONTEL
Tío, Hermano de Carmen
Uncle, Carmen's Brother

MIRANDA FLORES MONTEL
Tía, Hermana de Carmen
Aunt, Carmen's Sister

VICTORIA RAMIREZ MONTEL
Tía, Esposa de Joel
Aunt, Joel's Wife

FERNANDO MADERO
Tío, Uncle

SAMUEL MADERO
Tío, Uncle

LEO MADERO
Tío, Uncle

DANIEL MADERO
Tío, Uncle

GLORIA RODRÍGUEZ MADERO
Tía, Aunt

JESSICA MADERO
Tía, Aunt

EMMA MADERO
Tía, Aunt

RICARDO RODRÍGUEZ
Papi, Dad

ESPERANZA MADERO RODRÍGUEZ
Mami/Protagonista, Mom/Protagonist

VALENTINA RODRÍGUEZ
Hermana/Sister

AMELIA RODRÍGUEZ
Yo/Autora, Me/Author

RICKY RODRÍGUEZ
Hermano/Brother

Contents

Preface

April 2018

Time passes and I don't know how to begin. 1:00 p.m., 1:23 p.m., 1:53 p.m., 2:23 p.m.

Long stretches of silence mark the time. I haven't moved from my seat. My journal is open in front of me while I bob my head to the same song on repeat, twirling my pen. This is all I've written.

I'm writing a story, one full of so much estranged emotion that it could only be found hidden in the depths of people's private lives and histories. Yet, on the rare occasions we dive into the dark abysses and explore their depth, light shines upon them, revealing the complexity of their truth, and we become unafraid. Our deepest fears, worries, and guilts are understood and become our allies. Stepping into hope, we hold in our minds the answer to a life of love, light, forgiveness, empathy, and more love. When we dive deep, we come to realize the possibilities of our own consciousness.

The thing is, the stories do not get any easier to read or tell. As you go through this book, they will punch you in the gut, one right after the other. I write, however, so the truth may be heard. I write so my mom may further her healing. I write so I may heal, and my family may heal, and all affected by my abuelito may heal. I write for those who have survived sexual abuse, rape, physical violence, mental abuse, and more. I hope this book helps you find even more strength within you. Know you are not alone and that the beauty of life is all around. It may feel impossible but with effort, focus, and much practice, you can see that beauty. Though at times you may feel enslaved to your own thought cycles, you *can* come to master the patterns of your mind. According to the physician and trauma expert Gabor Mate, from his book *In the Realm of Hungry Ghosts*, "We may not be responsible for the world that created our mind, but we can take responsibility for the mind with which we create our world."

Use that power. Lean into the human potential to be your own healer. Lean on others — support is vital. But in the end, no one but yourself can keep your light shining.

So, I sit, engulfed in my own despair, unsure what to make of how I feel. Just feeling. Not sure how to understand what bubbles and mixes inside of me. Shouldn't this state fuel me as a writer, regardless of the black, wrenching emptiness that boils from seemingly nowhere? I keep my breathing constant. Just breathing. Then, out of the nothingness, a tiny breath saves me, trickling in a calm, blanketed wave of peace. Happiness ensues, as a smile appears on my face, sending a message of tranquility through my veins, straight into my heart.

I remember the beginning. The pureness of my being. The weightlessness of my light. I remember that I am free. I feel the essence of me, just within my reach — floating above me, around me, under me, through me. The realization flashes before me, as it often does throughout life, that I am always here for me. That I exist despite the dark. That I exist within the dark. I am, and so I shall always be, as long as I allow myself to sink into the love of my light.

I close my eyes, tears emerging from the corners, falling slowly. I smile as I feel the ache in my chest, welcoming it, allowing it to wash over me, so I may pay my dividends to the pain that has clearly also made me. I give the darkness its voice, acknowledging its being, and so it washes and washes, becoming, morphing, twisting, dancing into light.

WHERE SILENCE ENDS

Silence Imposed

1

In 1920, in the beautiful little town of Purepero, Michoacán, Mexico, the revolution was coming to an end. Emiliano Zapata, the leader and hero of the peasants' revolution, had just been assassinated. The tumultuous energy of the war was settling, as men and women begrudgingly returned to life before the uprising. Men journeyed on horseback, bringing crops back into town from the fields, kicking dust up behind them as they trotted down the dirt roads, ready to rebuild after losing their champion of change.

One summer afternoon, as the sun beamed down, the smell of fresh tortillas drifted out of the adobe homes, filling the streets with the sweetness of corn.

Against the front door of her home, a beautiful young girl of 14 years waited nervously in a white hand-stitched blouse and long dark blue skirt. Her hair was pinned up in a loose dark brown bun, her piercing green eyes accentuated by her light complexion. She was wild, fierce, and yet sweet as can be. Her love for life was contagious. Her name was Elena Esperanza Sánchez Valenzuela.

Elena had two boyfriends, Enrique and Hector, though they mainly functioned as pen pals, given the era and their age. After little contemplation, Elena made her choice: She wanted to be with Enrique, and therefore needed to end it with Hector. Leaning against the wooden door, she watched Hector approach.

"Hi Elena. You look beautiful," greeted Hector.

"Thank you, Hector. I'm glad you're here," established Elena.

As he began to remark on the day's mundanities, she shifted her face towards the sun. Soaking in the daylight, she let the warmth fill her soul, knowing the heartbreak she was about to evoke on the man before her. But a life of discovery and excitement awaited her, and she gushed with fondness for her Enrique. She took a deep breath and closed her eyes for a second longer to channel the sun's power, imagining the rays giving her the strength she needed. When she finally opened her eyes, they immediately met Hector's.

"Hector, I don't think we should be together anymore. I want to break up," she blurted out. For what seemed like an eternity, she waited nervously for a response, never breaking their stare.

Hector's body revved up. His insides were flooded with heat. His heart raced. His eyes narrowed in despise, as confusion and anger flooded his body. In a flash of rage, he reacted, lunging forward and grabbing Elena by her hair. In an instant, he threw her on the ground and began dragging her down the dirt road.

With his free hand, he pulled his gun out of his holster and pressed it up against the side of her head, hauling her onward with alarming ease. Elena screamed, curled up, and went limp. She was in shock and hoped her dead body weight would make it harder for him, but it seemed to only give him more strength, as he forcefully yanked her on, more rage and determination with every step. She gripped onto his forearms as her head and neck jerked to his violent rhythm, her scalp stinging and her knees skinning against the pebbles and rocks of the rugged road.

With every impact, cuts and gashes opened down her legs, arms, and torso, running the blood slowly out of her body. She wailed as he continued to drag her farther from home. Her breathing became heavy and strained, but despite his tight grip, she did not give up. She screamed louder, kicked harder, until finally, her alarming cries brought neighbors running out of their homes.

"Get back! Get back or I'll shoot her in the head!" Hector pointed the gun furiously at everyone who emerged. "If she does not marry me, I will finish her off!" Hector roared his demands, his deep and impassioned voice reverberating through the streets.

Neighbors yelled frantically, enraged and afraid. Fearful that Elena would be killed, if not kidnapped, raped, and forced to marry, they pleaded with him to let her go.

Elena's body throbbed with horror and hatred as she took in her surroundings. Everything slowed to a blurred whisper and all she could hear were her panicked breaths as he pressed the gun harder against her temple. Her eyes narrowed, looking out at the familiar faces of agony begging for his cooperation, pleading for her life. Her fate flashed before her: *Death, rape, or marriage to an evil man.*

She felt her body jerk as Hector jolted her to her feet, tears streamed down her face. Staring at the crowd he gathered, Hector contemplated his choices: *Let her go and force her to marry later when tensions and outrage subside, take her now and rape and marry her, or kill her now in the dusty streets.*

Knowing his male power was not in threat, Hector decided to let Elena go, but not without making sure she kept to his demands. "If you don't marry me, I will kill you and your family," he whispered maniacally in her ear, pressing her body close against his. She winced while he kissed her on the cheek, opened his grip, and set her free... for now.

She ran to the closest neighbors, collapsing into their arms, sobbing, bloody, and bruised. After collecting herself in their solace, she sprinted back down the street to her mother, where she broke down all over again.

Bride kidnappings, or "bridenappings," were not uncommon during the first half of the 20th century in Mexico. In fact, it still happens today, and not only in Mexico. But there, and all around the world, a man would, quite literally, snatch up the woman he wished to marry and rape her. He would then propose marriage, and she would likely say yes. Certainly not out of hopeless romance. Rather, because living under a regime of machismo, women were coerced into marrying their rapist, led to believe that after being raped they were worthless to other men. Virgin brides were prized. Women had very little power, their voices were regularly silenced, their feelings rarely considered. Not nearly enough progress has been made to change these tides, but this was the height of machismo culture and women knew they had two options: submit and live, or fight and risk violent rape and/or death.

Elena was not one to submit easily, and so she fought, knowing she had a long life of fighting ahead of her.

The following day, as was custom, Hector's father, Señor Madero, went to Elena's home, accompanied by a priest, to ask for her hand in marriage. Elena's mother, Señora Valenzuela-Sánchez, slowly opened the door with her three daughters lined up fearfully behind her. She greeted them sharply and reluctantly let them into her home, feeling she had no choice. Tensions high, Hector's father commenced: "We are here to ask for Elena's hand in marriage to our son, Hector."

Elena's mother was immediately filled with resentment, well aware of the brutal events from the day before, having soothed her distraught daughter to sleep. She spoke respectfully yet firmly, telling Señor Madero that her husband was currently working in the U.S. and it would take some time to give him a response.

Señor Madero nodded in agreement, understanding the man of the house had final say. He walked out of the Sánchez home with the priest, knowing he and his son would have to be patient for an answer.

Elena's mother sent a letter to her husband in a rush, sadly and nervously holding no details back. Upon receiving the letter and learning his daughter was taken against her will, ruthlessly abused, and was now being asked for her hand in marriage by her very abuser, he started devising a plan that would buy his daughter and family time. Still, he knew his daughter might be destined for a rough reality no matter his answer.

He wrote back: *Elena may not get married until I return. I will give her hand in marriage to Hector, but they must wait for me.* This was not what he or his wife wanted for their little girl, but he felt powerless in the confines of a conservative society and feared for his family's safety.

It took Elena's father five years to return to Mexico. He refused to come back any sooner, delaying the inevitability of his daughter's dreaded marriage. In the end, however, the choice would be Elena's, and hers alone. She was 19 when her father finally returned home.

"Mija, you do not have to marry this man," he told his daughter wishfully grasping.

She looked up at him with water in her eyes and fear in her body: "Yes I do. If I don't, he has made it clear that he will kill me or our family."

Elena's father's rage for Hector grew. He stared at his beautiful daughter, looking scared and hopeless. She was still his little girl. Determined to get Elena out of this arrangement, he offered another option.

"No, we can all flee the country, at night, and go to the United States. He will never see you again. You do not have to worry."

But she did worry. The conflict churning inside showed on her face, in her eyes. Purepero was the only home Elena had ever known. She grappled with her father's proposition and the thought of fleeing with only her immediate family. They would be leaving a close-knit community of aunts, uncles, cousins, and grandparents behind, never to see them again. They would have to start all over. Elena worried for her extended family's safety. Hector's voice never ceased to echo in her mind: *If you don't marry me, I will kill you and your family.*

She decided to marry.

Elena's parents exhausted the discussion with her, trying to make sense of their daughter's decision. They prepared her with what wisdom they could muster leading up to the wedding, somberly searching for a dress and organizing what would be a traditional two-day spectacle. Elena began accepting her fate. A violent start with her soon-to-be husband, in what she thought would be their last encounter, would set the cadence for the rest of their relationship.

On June 15th, 1926, Elena and Hector were married. Sadness poured from Elena's soul. She wore a frown all the way down the aisle, and throughout the event, Enrique still on her mind. Hector celebrated enthusiastically and greedily, with misplaced pride.

Looking out at the celebration before her, Elena mourned life as she knew it, preparing for the tumultuous road ahead. She knew she would need to work hard for happiness by her new husband's side. She just didn't know quite how hard.

❧

Elena was pregnant with their first child when Hector left to work in the United States, not to return for nine years. He sent money back when he could — or when he felt like it — but it would either get lost, stolen, or take ages to arrive. It was common back then to leave your family to go work in the United States for the promise of higher pay and a better life for all your loved ones. But not necessarily for nine years. Many men did have two families, though, one in each country. Like many taboos of the era, it was rarely spoken about, rather known in tormented silence.

Back in Purepero, Elena went into labor, alone. She gave birth to a boy, and it was no matter; the boy would be named after his father. Thus, Hector Madero II was born.

In spite of the heaviness in Elena's life, as a single mother with little financial support, Elena rose to become a town medicine woman and prominent healer. She adapted plant and herbal recipes handed down through generations, and learned from traveling doctors, growing most of what she needed in her own backyard. She was securing her place in life, establishing herself financially so she could provide for her child without a husband around. Little Hector was her love, and to distract from her hardships, she sang him songs of the revolution, songs of silver linings. She sang herself through motherhood, holding onto the flashes of light that turned the broken pieces of herself into treasures.

By the time Hector returned to Mexico, his nine-year-old son was a mix of joy and nerves to meet his father for the first time. Despite an inaugural embrace, Little Hector found his fate to quickly resemble his mother's. Hector demanded Little Hector love and respect him from the start. Beating the macho man mentality into his son regularly, Hector triggered a violent beast within that forever stayed with his son and impacted every life he would go on to touch.

The shock and whiplash of being the man of the house for his first nine years only to be physically beaten into his subordinate role as son diminished Little Hector. His eyes and ears exposed to his father's daily abuse of his mother added a layer of core trauma to his being. The foundation of love he and his mother spent his childhood building was shattered by his cruel father, who squandered every ounce of their warmth and affection for each other.

His mother was forced to rely on her husband where she once relied on her son. To make matters worse, Hector forced Elena and Little Hector to move from living with Elena's family, who were loving and warm, to living with his own, who were aggressive and hostile. The grooming grounds for Little Hector were set. The combination of shock and trauma at such a young age laid a new, villainous foundation over his mother's nine years of vested love and generosity — one that would forever change Little Hector. His father's rotten roots began to spoil his purity, wrapping around his youthful soul, and eclipsing his mother's roots of genuine love. A young man with mysterious darkness was emerging.

Elena and Hector had three more children after Little Hector, two sons and a daughter. The parents spread their seeds the only way they each knew how: one with love and one with evil, and so it began.

2

It was 1946 and Little Hector was not so little anymore. He was 17 and learning to juggle his violent fantasies in a reality that lived outside of the public eye. The grip of machismo culture aided in Hector's ability to remain unseen for the true villain that, over the years, he had become. Only his masculine dominance showed through and was reliably glorified by those around him. The evil that quietly emerged within was violently punched, whipped, and pummeled into him over the past eight years by his father. He adopted his father's entitlement to do what he wanted with bodies that were not his to claim. He watched in fear as his father physically, mentally, and even sexually dominated his mother, Elena. He listened as rumors floated around about his father forcing himself on other young women in town. He endured his father's trauma through blows to his growing body and mind.

The Maderos were partly of Spanish descent, and it was evident that the violent entitlement to other people's bodies and lives came, partly, from centuries of Spanish conquest. And though Little Hector may not have liked his father's ways, he grew to embody his father's vision of a man. At 17, he split his time between family in Purepero and attending boarding school two hours away in Morelia.

Unbeknownst, his future wife lived right around the corner from his family's home. Her name was Carmen Flores Montel, and at 13, she spent her days playing on the dirt roads with other neighborhood kids, innocent and joyful. In the small town of Purepero, financial strife did not impede happiness. Life was simple, people were relaxed, and the kids played in the streets until late without a worry.

One delightful evening, Hector walked by Carmen and her friends with a group of his own. Carmen caught his eye in the setting sun, and he stared at her admiringly, observing her playful childlike spirit. He held onto the feeling of butterflies in his stomach, telling his friends: "She will be mine one day. She will definitely be mine."

Meanwhile, Carmen was completely oblivious to Hector, let alone his adoration for her. She was too focused on helping her family at home and playing with friends. She had only made it to second grade when her parents pulled her out of school to help her mother run the household full-time.

As the eighth of 13 children, and the first girl, Carmen naturally took on a maternal role at home. It was while she learned to prepare dinner for her family of 15 that her love of cooking was born. She was delighted to share this space with her mother.

"What are we going to make today, mamá? Tortas de papa?" Carmen smiled and her dark brown eyes lit up her fair skin, while her dark brown hair draped her small frame. Carmen's mother was kind, loving, and a great teacher who enjoyed passing her recipes down to her firstborn daughter. Carmen was surrounded with love.

Her godmother lived next door and popped in often. One day, her godmother approached her in the kitchen and asked for help in preparing the meal for her nephew's baptism. Carmen gladly agreed. While she helped her godmother prepare atole and tamales, her gaze floated up, landing on a striking young man walking through the front door. It was Hector.

He was delivering goods as a favor to her godmother. Their eyes met for an instant. Carmen shyly smiled and looked away bashfully. She thought to herself: I am going to marry that man one day. Her young intuition was strong, but it would be a couple years before they would begin a relationship, and many more before he would annihilate her intuition altogether.

Carmen's father, also fair skinned, had bright blue eyes and grounded the family with his warmth and calm. The years passed peacefully in their kitchen, until tragedy struck when Carmen was 15. Her mother had a stroke, paralyzing the right side of her body. She began relying heavily on Carmen around the house — cooking, cleaning, and taking care of her younger siblings.

Despite her youth and innocence, she took the responsibility on with pride, eager to help her parents she so loved and admired. The entire family suffered as they watched their beloved matriarch slowly deteriorate. The worry and stress became enormous for Carmen, who developed high blood pressure as a young teenager. To hide her constant state of despair and red eyes, she would splash water on her face throughout the day. Nothing could help the excruciating fact that she was losing her mother.

Carmen's mother would lift her lifeless arm with her able right, hoping to have the strength to keep it in the air, purely to have it slam against her body time and time again. Watching and weeping while her mother tried to outsmart her paralysis, Carmen yearned to go back and freeze time to keep her mother healthy. Instead, she was beyond repair.

Carmen distracted herself from the agony at home with a busy social life, family gatherings, cooking, and her sprouting romance with her godmother's delivery boy. Hector and Carmen had officially started dating. She was falling madly in love with this young man who was a leader in his pack and respected by many. Carmen was not yet aware of Hector's well-hidden demons, and so she sailed the harsh waves of her mother's declining health together with Hector, and all the changes that came along with the storm.

In the summer of 1949, Carmen turned 16. With the difficulty of appearing strong for her family amidst the sorrow of slowly losing her mother, Hector was her strongest support. His family and friends adored her all the same, welcoming her into their lives with open arms, frequently fawning: "You are going to marry Little Hector one day!"

At 17, Carmen was falling deeper in love with Hector, with her mother losing steam every day. All she could do was dream of one day forming her own family with Hector, even though she knew it would mean leaving her siblings and parents behind. It would not be easy, but she knew the day would come, and it did.

One September morning, as the skies stretched a clear blue with patches of pearl white clouds, the couple stood against Carmen's family home, excited by their growing bond. Life bustled all around them — bakers in big rimmed wicker hats holding freshly baked bread for sale shuffled along; women walking in traditional long skirts and rebosos wrapped around their top half went about their errands; men wearing huaraches, white linen suits, and straw hats led their donkeys with bundles of wood on their backs. The smell of fresh dough from bakeries mingled with the spice of burning chili, sweet hints of cinnamon, and freshly roasted corn. Amidst the vivacity of Purepero, Hector nervously looked at Carmen and mustered the courage to say the words that she wished for.

"I love you. I want to marry you," Hector stated. An enormous smile spilled across her face, as she floated and nodded in agreement. He informed Carmen that he would send the priest to her house the following day to ask her parents for her hand in marriage. They embraced before parting ways to excitedly await the next sunrise.

Carmen walked back into her home but decided against sharing the news with her family. However excited she was, an empty sadness was never far from reach, all too aware of her mother's rapid decline. One of Carmen's sisters-in-law was there and insisted she come over the next morning to visit. Knowing the priest was to arrive around the same time, but ever the people-pleaser, Carmen accepted the invitation, leaving the rest up to fate.

Sure enough, the priest arrived the next morning, and to his surprise, Carmen was not there. She was down the street, anxiously making tortillas with her sister-in-law, but Hector's proposal hadn't left her mind. Soon, her brother walked in with a smirk on his face.

"Carmen, there was a visitor looking for you at mom and dad's earlier."

She turned to her sister-in-law and frantically blurted: "Ay Diana! Hector told me he was going to send the priest to ask for my hand in marriage this morning!"

Diana amusingly replied: "And you escaped him, Carmen?!"

The three of them burst into laughter, Carmen's sounding slightly more nervous. "Well, yes. I guess I did escape. What if Hector no longer asks for my hand? I guess we will see if it was truly meant to be. Only God knows."

And so, she left it up to God whether Hector would send the priest back the following day, or if he would withdraw his proposal after her mini escape. Sure enough, the priest returned. Carmen was delighted, yet nervous about taking this next step in life, not quite ready to leave her family.

She stood next to her father as the priest asked for her hand in marriage on Hector's behalf. Carmen's father looked at her calmly with his bright blue eyes, and she realized the decision was hers, and the time was now or never to make it. Ultimately, her love for Hector outweighed her nerves. She took a deep breath, smiled, and nodded to her father, signaling her acceptance.

Carmen's father told the priest his family would accept the proposal with a year-long engagement, given her young age. Carmen smiled to herself, happy and excited about the future.

As the end of Carmen and Hector's year-long engagement inched near, Carmen's mother slipped further into her physical sickness, until one day, a stroke stormed her body, sweeping her away forever. Maria Montel Flores passed before turning fifty. With her death, the clouds turned a dense grey. The skies descended into blackness. Rain poured inside Carmen's heart. The ancient traditional Roman Catholic novena, when loved ones gather for nine consecutive days to pray for the soul of the deceased, was set in motion. On the first night, the coffin lay in the middle of the living room, awaiting the burial the following day.

Carmen watched her younger siblings cry out: "Mamá! Mamá!" with torment in their little voices, returning to their mother's body over and over again to caress her face and weep. Carmen ached for them losing their mother so young, ached for herself to lose the most important figure in her life, but she could not bring herself to the open casket. Feeling broken and in a daze, she stared at her mother's corpse from a distance, and sobbed quietly.

The little ones pleaded with Carmen not to get married and leave the house. They felt they were losing yet another mother and it weighed on Carmen until she cried her way to a resolution. Days after her mother's funeral, Hector was consoling Carmen, holding her and giving her the space to cry, when she looked up at him and said: "I will not get married until it has been one year since the day of my mother's passing."

He responded without hesitation: "I will wait that time for you and more." She put her head back on his chest and cried some more, her love expanding for him.

Over the days and months that followed, Carmen dressed in all black. The next year of her life was spent at home looking after her younger siblings and father; it was a year of mourning and anxiety.

With her mother, Carmen lost a part of herself. She lost her will to fight. The year ended and the day for her to get married arrived.

Carmen and Hector wed in the church of Purepero in the summer of 1952 at the absurd hour of seven o'clock in the morning, as was custom. The church bells rang across town, solidifying the newlyweds' eternal union. The birds soared above as the mariachi walked the couple and their guests out of the church, through the town, and to the reception. Breakfast was served with hot chocolate, sweet bread, and more mariachi.

Always a maker of bold fashion statements, Carmen wore a white pantsuit on her wedding day — a daring move, especially in an era when womanhood was so deeply rooted in femininity. But this taste for style was really an obsession with status, and arguably her greatest downfall. Before it took her down, however, it was the star of the ceremony of a union both families rejoiced. Carmen's father entrusted his daughter to Hector Madero II, thrilled that she chose who he thought was a well-respected, hardworking, and spirited man to spend her life with. Luckily for him, he would not be around to discover the roots of rot that grew stronger by the day inside his son-in-law.

After the reception, Carmen and Hector took off on their honeymoon to Guadalajara. The newlyweds planned an eight-day getaway but ended up returning on the fifth day. Carmen's nerves got the best of her. She was never spoken to about sex, and comprehended little of the act, but she knew that this was the occasion she was to lose her virginity. The shock of this hit her body like a massive wave and she shut down. She could not eat anything, feeling only the need to vomit. Her body sent signals of alarm throughout. She was nervous — nervous to have sex for the first time with the man she loved.

"Let's go home! You're going to die on me like this!" Hector declared. And so, they did. Upon their return to Purepero, Hector went straight to his mother. "Mamá! Carmen's sick! She has not wanted to eat anything." His father quickly joined the conversation from the kitchen table.

"Oooh, but my new daughter will eat right away!" The joy and sense of love Carmen felt from her new family seemed to calm her nerves and gave her strength to begin eating again.

It did not take long for her to settle into the comfort of her new life with a radiating sense of happiness. Soon Carmen and Hector began trying for a family of their own and she became pregnant. They were ecstatic with the uplifting joy of a baby forming inside her, but a few months into the pregnancy, her body miscarried. Devastated, they kept on trying. Carmen became pregnant again, bringing the couple high hopes and unending nerves. The first two months passed smoothly, until the third month hit, and the couple was confronted with their second miscarriage.

Heavy sadness and uncertainty enveloped Carmen and Hector, but they endured with the force of nature driving their desire to procreate in love. Finally, their third pregnancy was a success and Carmen gave birth to a son, Fernando. The pair was ecstatic and blissful celebrating their firstborn.

Two years into parenthood, Hector followed in his father's footsteps and began traveling back and forth between Purepero and California for work in agriculture. He was forced to leave Carmen and their toddler son behind for months at a time — but never years. Unlike his father, Hector returned as often as he could to be with his growing family.

In 1958, Hector's boss proposed an idea. Knowing Hector to be an exceptionally hard and dedicated worker, he offered to move Hector and his family to the United States to work full-time in Southern California. Hector would work as a driver, picking and dropping off workers from the agriculture fields, as well as a farmer, cultivating tomatoes. After speaking to Carmen about the proposal, it was impossible for them not to accept. The couple excitedly yet anxiously agreed, wishful for greater opportunities for their family. That summer, they were moved to Huntington Beach, California.

Hector and his family moved under the Bracero program — an agreement signed between the U.S. and Mexico to help the U.S. with the shortage of agricultural workers because of WWII — requiring Hector's bosses to cover moving expenses, decent and free shelter, meals, occupational insurance, and transportation to work. Having a boss who actually appreciated him, Hector was one of the lucky ones. His boss, Griffith, went above and beyond to honor the regulations in the agreement and gave Hector and Carmen a charming and spacious ranch to live on. They felt like they hit the jackpot.

But life is never as it seems, and we are in a constant state of motion. Change is around every corner, and not all change is good. All things must come to an end of what they once were, in order to take their place in the present moment and become what is.

3

Over the next five years, Carmen and Hector's clan grew. Their siblings from Mexico slowly joined them, family by family in Huntington Beach — some through the Bracero program, others not. They were elated with their growing family in the states, despite experiencing the heartache of two more miscarriages after Fernando. Finally, after years of trying to get pregnant, in the winter of 1961, Carmen gave birth to her first and only daughter: Esperanza Madero.

She came five years after Fernando and was the first Madero born in the United States, followed by three more boys: Samuel, Leo, and Daniel. The five became a tribe of siblings, all of them handsome and stylish in their own ways. They were like the Mexican Jackson Five, friends would joke.

Fernando was the leader of the pack and the disciplinarian to his four younger siblings. He would become the playful, loud, and tough-love uncle. Esperanza was sweet, obedient, outgoing, and a nurturing soul to her band of brothers. She would become the lioness with the loudest roar. Samuel, born nearly exactly a year after Esperanza, was the protector. He was also the neighborhood's heart throb, and would become the strong, outspoken, yet sensitive uncle. Samuel and Esperanza were best pals, sharing many of the same friends. Their closeness in age gave them a particularly special bond among the five.

The two youngest, Leo and Daniel, were also a bit of a duo, constantly getting into trouble, creating the kind of wild memories that kids, nieces, and nephews love to hear a generation later. Leo was tall and quiet, yet aggressive when he wanted to be. He would become the stern adult who was trusted by all. Daniel, the youngest of the clan, was loud, mischievous, and took after his mother with a love and skill for cooking. He was a tractor-riding expert, always wearing black leather jackets, bandanas, and leather boots. He would become the cool uncle with a playful nature.

Together, a little Mexican girl and her four brothers were raised in Huntington Beach, California, a sunny surfer town in the United States of America. Life seemed to be flourishing for the Madero family in this new country. They were learning the language, finding their place, and letting the sun warm them from the outside in — for now. But the coldness at the core of the man at the center was beginning to seep out.

Hector Madero II was the patriarch of the entire Madero clan. He was loud, confident, blunt, and immensely loved, trusted, and respected. He was the natural-born leader of his and Carmen's blended families, his word the final one amongst the men. He commanded everybody and everything. The community of families he and Carmen led to California leaned heavily on them for support, guidance, and lively entertainment.

For Saturday picnics in the park, the adults bought what Hector told them to buy. If someone opposed, he would argue them into submission. He always won, in everything.

Hector was tall, broad, with hazel eyes and a perfectly combed thick mustache. His belly was that of a man who ate well but was strong. Though he maintained a heroic facade, Hector's evil nature would eventually rise to the surface. The bitter and resentful silence he kept around his own childhood traumas handcuffed him to the rock bottom of his own dark abyss, hiding his evil madness from the world. This same silence bred hostility and his father's rage and entitlement, as the rotting roots of his family tree curled around him tightly, suffocating all of his light, until he became pure darkness. Everything other than darkness was a front. His family had not yet met the beast lurking within, and still worshiped his every move.

Meanwhile, Carmen leaned into her passion for cooking, whipping up Mexican, American, Italian, Chinese dishes, and more. Heavenly aromas permeated the Madero home, nourishing their family and friends, and enticing a constant flow of company. The Madero home was the place to be, with music always blaring and drinks ever-flowing. Carmen was a figurehead in her own rite, greatly loved, trusted, and respected amongst the wives. When there was a party, even if Carmen and Hector were not the hosts, guests would arrive to greet them first. They were the pillars of their community. Carmen always dressed the best, with her hair and make-up perfect, and her long natural fingernails consistently painted a blood red. She was the spitting image of the dazzling centerfold housewife from Mexican novelas — beautiful big brown eyes, a fashion sense to kill, and short hair that sat on her head like a 70s queen. Although she was far from a queen you would ever want to call your own.

No one could have imagined the horrors going on inside her home. Not even her own sons.

There was a hell burning, and from what I would learn, it never stopped. My mother was born in a fiery jungle, entangled at the bottom of a vast dark abyss by the predatory vines of some of her ancestors. Forced to navigate her way through, she came to understand the ways of evil by being wrapped in it her whole life. Squirming her way out of the rotting roots that suffocated her, splitting the mangled vines wrapped around her tightly, bit by bit, breath by breath, she freed herself, and freed her soul — planting new roots that sprouted up towards the light in a fresh jungle of her own. She was destined to survive, focusing on the good she never stopped believing in.

Silence Manipulated

4

I was born in Huntington Beach, California, in 1986. I am first-generation
in the U.S. on my dad's side and second-generation on my mom's. The
Mexican in me runs deep, surging through every stream of blood in my
body, the very fiber of my bones, and sitting with an everlasting smile in
my soul. My name is Amelia Rodriguez and I am Esperanza's second child
— the middle child, which is apparently going extinct. Unlike the oldest
and youngest child, the middle child has a reputation for being deeply
emotional, sometimes to excess. I relate. In the case of this book, this
quality has allowed me to plunge passionately into writing this disturbing,
twisted, and yet tremendously inspirational story about my family. No
matter how dark your history may be, learning the stories of blood relatives
who came before is empowering beyond belief. Exploring my family's
history has been one of the greatest gifts I could give to myself, to my
mom, and the Madero legacy. I am proud of how this story has shaped us.
I am most of all proud of my mom. I stand beside her, smiling that I am
the daughter of a champion of unparalleled grace and strength.

My mother and I talked as we drove through the suburbs of
Huntington Beach, CA, half a mile from the ranch where she was born.
She had not been back to that neighborhood in decades. As we got closer
to where the ranch was located, I could feel the tension mounting,
vibrating out of my throat, chest, back, and toes.
  I guided my mom through the idyllic neighborhoods, lined with well-
tended gardens and stucco homes, with the help of Google maps.
  "It says we've arrived," I said with confusion.
  My mom looked around but did not recognize her surroundings. A
school had been built close to where her home once stood. I felt a
surprising sense of disappointment, realizing the area did not even slightly

resemble the pictures in the album on my lap, nor my mother's memories. Decades of social evolution turned what was once a compound of ranches into an elementary school. I couldn't help but think: *Thank God this school was not here when Abuelito Hector was living here.*

We parked across from the school and made ourselves comfortable. It was January 11th, 2013. Crows called to one another overhead, flying from tree to tree, as a cool breeze swirled gently through the cracked windows of my mom's white SUV. It was a gorgeous afternoon with the sun shining brightly and the shade of a tree on the sidewalk providing cool relief as we leafed through the photo album of my mom's early childhood. I stared at a black and white photo of her at four months old, the date marked below with a pencil: April 1962. Her older brother, Fernando, held her while they sat on the hood of their dad's truck. The two siblings looked happy.

The next picture shifted our attention uncomfortably. It was Abuelito Hector. I pointed to it and looked up. "When you see this picture, how does it make you feel?"

She took a deep breath: "It makes me feel like erasing him out of my life. I wish I could delete him out of the picture."

She let out a heavy sigh and went on sharing: "Here's another picture. I never glued this one in. The others seemed easier, but this one, because my father was holding me, was difficult to include. I put it in because I liked the picture of my brothers and me."

It was a picture of her at 14 and her dad at 46. She was in the center, seated on a stool in the backyard of their home. Her three younger brothers stood around her playfully, their father right behind her, reaching his arm around the front of her body, clutching her hand in his, pulling her close to his body. She wore one of the coolest 70s outfits I could imagine: red halter top and hot pants, with small white flowers scattered across both. She was squinting, half-smiling in the picture. Her beauty made you forget about the grotesque feeling the picture ignited, however briefly. Her prominent dark curly hair, almond-shaped hazel eyes, and lean young figure were impossible not to admire. Still, it made us both uncomfortable. Even 35 years later, the picture was profoundly unsettling.

I felt deeply proud of my mom for sharing her story with me and confronting this torturous and excruciating part of her past. Writing this book was her idea, one of her life's dreams, and she wanted to do it together, knowing my love for writing. She first proposed it to me when I was just 16. As I polish the final draft, it is 2020 (the year of global reckoning with troubling truths) and I am 33.

More than anything though, I was an emotional mess of nerves, anger, and fear, my entire body turning into a furnace every time I asked a question, dreading the horror of every answer. I had heard some of these stories before, but they never got easier to listen to. It was only a few days prior that I made the conscious decision to dive deeper into this part of my family history and create this book. I can still hear the sound of air filling my chest as I composed my breath and forced myself to ask: "At what age did the sexual abuse begin?"

"Oh, I was little. I was actually digging through my stuff earlier and found my old journal that I started in the early 90s. You must have been four years old. My therapist at the time encouraged me to write. For years, I covered it in a pillowcase. Pulling it out today was a big step." She told me how she stood around the journal for a bit, took a picture of it in the pillowcase, stood around it for another while before finally taking the pillowcase off forever — and snapping another picture of the journal, uncovered. She handed it to me.

I looked down and saw an image of Garfield, the orange cat, screeching and jumping in complete surprise — apt for the appalling content inside.

"I recognize this journal!" I said laughing. "You let me read it once."

"Yes, I did," she said chuckling.

Before opening it, my mind raced back to when I was a sophomore in high school and caught my mom reading my own journal entries.

It was a sunny afternoon in 2002. I returned home from school and immediately threw my red Jansport backpack down on the living room couch and I wandered around the house aimlessly like I did most days. When I returned to the living room, my mom was standing over my backpack, snooping through my spiraled blue journal. I was furious, shouting that my privacy had been violated. And like many 16-year-olds would do, I stormed out of the house and did not come back for a few hours.

I knew my mom felt bad by the look on her face when I caught her, but it was even more evident when I walked into my room that night to find the Garfield journal I was holding now, lying on my bed. I froze in my tracks. My breathing instantly became slow, deep, and loud, anchoring me to the moment. This was her way of saying: "I'm sorry for invading your privacy. Here are my deepest secrets in return." I stood staring, debating whether to open it or not. Chills broke out down my body.

I was aware of my mom's history with her father, but I never dug for details. I knew there were going to be plenty of entries that would make me want to scream, sob, and become angry. I felt lightheaded and my eyes started to water before I could move. With a deep breath I switched the main light off and stepped towards the journal, grabbing it and slowly getting into bed.

I turned my bedside lamp on, leaving the blinds open to reveal the dark starry sky. I propped myself up with pillows, got under the blankets, and opened it up. For hours, I read and re-read. Crying. Sobbing. Trying to find a rhythm of breath that would not make me feel like I was drowning. I finally fell asleep during the brief period the sky moved from darkness to light."

⚜

Here we were again, 11 years later, only this time, my mom and I opened up her journal together. Before she took it into her own hands to begin reading, she warned me there was bad language. I started laughing and told her whatever profanity she used was more than appropriate for what she was writing about. She cleared her throat and read aloud from her journal titled *There Is Hope*, from the first chapter titled *Me*, written in 1990.

I was born in the winter of 1961. The furthest back I can remember is when I was approximately four years old. I can remember my approximate age because of the house we lived in. I remember going up some stairs into a room. I now know this was the attic where one of my uncles — Tío Oscar — slept. He had his pants down and was making me have oral sex with him. I cannot recall if he touched me or not. When I think back to this point in my life, I feel deep down inside this was not the first time I was molested. I cannot recall Tío Oscar molesting me again, even though he lived with us for a while. At age 12, I can recall he showed me a book that showed different positions of making love. He asked if I would explain the book to him. I recall looking at him funny, and Tío Oscar said, 'I guess you're too young'. That was the end of that. I know my father started to molest me at a very young age, because at one point when I confronted my mother, she told me (this is so hard to write) that at age three, when she returned from her friends who cut her hair, she found me with a really bad vaginal rash. She said my father promised he would never do it again. I hate this, because while I'm writing, I have so much anger inside. I feel like I have a big lump in my throat, and am having trouble breathing. I cannot cry, but want to.

Another time I can recall is when I was about four or five years old. My father used to take my brother, who is one year younger than I, and myself to his work after hours, to an agricultural farm where people worked growing crops. He used to tell my mother we needed to play in the dirt because it was healthy. I can only recall myself laying on something, but don't remember what it was, fully nude or just my panties off, but I can recall my father putting his penis next to my private part. I don't know how much my father put his penis in.

"My body is heating up," my mom said before she let out a breath of exasperation. She put the journal down and looked up at me. "Over the years you try and forget, but when I go over specific memories, it all comes back into my head and I can picture everything. Sometimes you try and put it away, so it almost feels like it does not exist, but it's there. It is always there."

We stared at each other, knowing this was therapeutic for both of us, feeling safe in the environment we created together. Safe enough to delve into the details of a horrible past. After a few seconds, we smiled slightly at one another in reassurance. She looked down at her journal and proceeded.

At age five, I can recall everyone was in bed. My father was in the living room nude and had me laying on the sofa. My panties were off, and again his penis was touching my private part. I do not remember if his penis was partly in, or just touching me. I recall my mother coming out of her room. She was screaming, yelling and crying! My oldest brother came out of his room. He also saw what was going on. He was about ten at the time. He cried. My mother held me and did not want to let me go. She continued fighting with my father. She said she was not going to leave me alone, but my father finally took me from her arms and put me back in my own room where I slept alone in my own crib. The next day my older brother told me if my father touched me again, he was going to run away. I know I was constantly abused, but cannot remember each time.

———

This journal was my mom's main confidant. The keeper of her gravest secrets. And boy were they grave. My mother was sexually, physically, and verbally abused by her own father since she was a toddler. He also treated her as a maid, requiring her to clean the entire kitchen after every meal, starting at the age of five — among many other household chores. She would finish eating, drag her tiny self to the kitchen sink where her step stool awaited, and begin hours of cleaning. Washing everyone's dishes, all the pots, pans, and mopping up the floor, she would eagerly dream of playing in the next room with her brothers. Although she was in an atrocious situation, her soul was growing strong, and a love for life was beginning to push through.

My abuelitos were a big part of why my mom and I found ourselves parked across the street of this elementary school. Of course, my abuelitos are a huge part of this story, but please understand — this book is not simply intended to recount the perverse actions of Abuelito Hector, or the hideously grave errors of Abuelita Carmen. This book is about giving raw human insight into the lives of a family with generational trauma and the processes of restoration. It is about recognizing the endless emotional, mental, physical, and spiritual acrobatics people move through to cope with trauma — and how these strategies work differently for all of us.

It is about overcoming mental hardships daily, allowing your past to elevate you, allowing love to rule, and befriending anguish. It is about leading oneself through hell like a victorious warrior — no matter the wounds your predator ripped open within you. Do not give that predator the satisfaction of claiming you.

This story is about welcoming happiness, opening the heart to love, and feeling the flow of acceptance. Trauma and all its effects have a way of tightening around you, like the thorny vines of an ancient tree, deep in the forest where no one can hear you. You feel the weight of their bind. It becomes increasingly hard to breathe. The heavy vines continue wrapping with a firm grip, so tight that breaking free seems hopeless, tugging you down into an abyss of your own emotion. You settle into your wounds, surrendering to the crushing weight imposed on your mind, body, and soul. Slowly your weeping begins to release you. Your voice becomes stronger, and day by day you find that the hate this predator poured inside you turns to wild strength. My mom, and many others, show us it is possible to liberate yourself from these suffocating forces, break free and plant new seeds.

5

My father would often take me places with him in the car. While he drove he would pull his penis out and would lay me down and make me have oral sex with him. I hate him so much when I think back. During these times he would grab me by the hair and bring me down to him. That's pretty much it. I hate him so much. It makes me angry the things he would do to a child. A very, very young child. I was in elementary school. It was extremely hurtful. He never did it when anyone else was present.

My mom looked up to see how I was doing. I stared at her expressionless, allowing my insides to do the reacting — with outrage. She carried on reading.

I can recall, and this happened very often, when my mother would get upset at my father and after I ate my dinner, she would make me take him his dinner. I hated it because she and I both knew what was going to happen. I would ask why she didn't take it and she would yell at me and I would be forced to take him dinner to their bedroom. I always knocked on the door first. I would wait nervously until the door opened for me to go in. I always hoped he would get dressed, but he never did. I would try and just leave the plate but he would hit me and have me lay under the blankets with him next to his naked body. He would make me touch him. I know there must have been more, but I can't recall. That bothered me so much! My mom would ALWAYS send me to the room when she was upset at him, and she knew what was going to happen. It is not like she didn't know. I would go in and would not come out for a while. I was in elementary school.

I fought back tears, breathing deeply through my nose, closing my eyes for extended periods, unable to bear the world that created this terror. I slowly opened my eyes and smiled at my mom, slightly nodding my head to indicate I heard and understood all of the nefarious offenses she just described. I wanted to let her know I was still with her.

My mom grinned, reassuring me: "Abuelita Elena lived with us for a couple years after my abuelito passed and my life was a lot better. I was ten years old and my father was forced to be a lot sneakier because she would sleep in my room with me."

She was trying to make me feel better about the trauma she suffered. Still, even when Abuelita Elena lived with them, Abuelita Carmen would force my mom to take a dinner plate to the master bedroom, where her father waited with his clothes off — and of course Abuelita Elena thought nothing of it.

My mom looked down at her journal and pressed on.

My father, almost every night, walked into my room. It usually ended up being pretty late, after midnight. He would come next to my bed and pull my panties down. I would start crying and scaredly tell him to get out. He would hit me and shut me up, and that instilled a huge amount of fear in me. He would hit me from the time I was little. It is the only response I ever knew, and because of that, I was terrified of him. He would touch my private part and would then start kissing me there. I hated him. I would cry the whole time. My mom though, I'm sure she would wake up at times and realize he was gone or would even hear me cry a little, she had to. I was not able to sleep at night. I would wake up and my father would be touching me, so I learned not to sleep, starting in elementary school. That was my protection. I had to survive. If I was awake, especially as I got older, I had more of a chance.

She sighed sadly: "That is how I developed severe insomnia. If I stayed awake, there was a better chance of fighting him off and not getting molested. I had many sleepless nights as a child. The insomnia actually got worse as I got older and continues to be severe to this day. A good night's sleep for me is anywhere between three and four hours. It has been that way for most of my life. The effects are becoming evident in my health. I really hope to be able to sleep better one day. Anyways, you want me to continue reading?" She did not want to burden me with more horrors than I could handle.

I mustered up an: "Mmm," and nodded my head while my gut turned. I kept my breathing slow and regular to not overwhelm my body. She dove further into her past.

I can recall back to one day when my father, younger brothers, and I went to visit my favorite uncle, Tío Joel, my mother's brother, and his family. I was somewhere between seven and nine years old. We knocked but nobody was home, however somehow my father managed to get in. While my brothers were outside playing, my father took me inside. I don't recall to what part of the house, but I do recall he again pulled his stupid pants down and pulled off my panties while I cried. He told me to shut up or he would hit me. I was so scared of him that I would not yell. I'm so angry. I can't stop writing even though it is after midnight.

She looked up from the journal to meet my stone-cold gaze.

"That was another incident. He was like an animal. Everywhere, and any chance he would get," she said.

"Did he have sex with you?"

"Yes. From the time I was a small child."

My mother's words suspended me in time, and I forgot to breathe. I did not know how to react. After what seemed like a whole life's journey, I blurted out: "I did not know that!" How could I not though, after all these stories? A wave of ignorance slammed me, realizing I had never allowed my mind to slide that far down the rotting roots, to the bottom of this dark abyss, to associate the word 'sex' in the context of my mom and her father — until that moment.

"You did not know what?" My mom looked at me a bit confused.

"That he had sex with you." I shivered.

"Well, there's oral sex, which is considered sex. Then sex could be him putting his penis slightly in my vagina as well. I was a child. I never knew if he actually penetrated all the way when I was younger — I could have blocked it out — but I know my vagina was regularly covered in bad rashes. Around six years old, I came home from the beach, irritated by the sand, and to urinate stung so badly. I whined to my mom and she looked at me as if to say: 'Shut up! Don't say it!'

"All I was saying was that it stung. She knew why, but she would just give me a dirty look and not say a word. I don't know how far in my father would go, but does it matter? That is rape. It was constant rape from the time I was a child. Is that not sad?" she said contemplatively to her younger self.

"Did he ever penetrate all the way when you were older?" I asked, frightened of the answer.

"When I went into junior high, his behavior changed. He started performing oral sex on me instead of forcing me to do it to him. I developed my breasts at a young age, at thirteen, and his dirty ways evolved. As my body changed, so did his abuse. He moved away from putting his penis slightly in my vagina to touching me, feeling me, and having oral sex with me."

I started questioning out loud, not really directing the questions at my mom, but rather trying to process: "Just any chance he would get? Not caring that you were his daughter? Not caring that you were a little kid?"

"Yup. You want me to go on?" she asked.

"Mhmm." It was all my body could muster, motionless and heavy, my heart pounding against my chest, taking long deep breaths to stabilize myself.

We had a live-in babysitter, because my mom worked in the field with my father. I was between six and nine years old. I can recall my father calling me into the room at night. Not one or two or three nights, but often. I'm so upset but I can't cry. God, please, help me cry. He would either be nude or have his pants down and would make me have oral sex with him. He used to tell me I needed to get him ready for when my mom came to bed. Many times I would cry, and he would hit me so I would shut up. Then he would tell me before leaving his room, 'You better take the live-in sitter outside to the backyard,' and he would leave the draperies open while he had sex with my mother so that we could see from the backyard. The next day he would ask me if I took the girl. I say girl, because she was around 16 years old.

She stared at the page uncomfortably before looking up. "My father would ask me if I took the girl outside to watch him and my mom having intercourse. If I told him the drapes were closed, he would get super upset, hit me, and demand I take her out earlier the next day."

"And did, would it, did you…" I stumbled across my words in shock. I took another deep breath to collect my thoughts. "Did you ever have to sit there and actually watch them have sex?"

"Yeah! Several times," she exclaimed without pause. "We drove that girl to her house to drop her off one day and she was crying. I did not know why my parents were taking her home, since she lived with us, but now I realize my father probably molested her and my mom was blaming the girl. Or maybe my mom found out she was watching through the window, not realizing he opened the drapes and forced her to watch. That was more of my father's sick fantasy."

I am imagining the sheer fright and anxiety my mom must have felt at such a young age, not wanting to put this girl through such a horrifying experience of being forced to watch her parents engage in such an intimate adult act — naked, kissing, touching, having sex.

"Do you really think your mom didn't know the curtains were open?" I asked suspiciously.

"I don't think my mom knew. I heard her tell my father several times: 'Close those drapes, close those drapes!' and he would do it at her insistence. I am sure there were a handful of nannies he screwed up. He messed with so many people," she said adamantly.

"Geez," I let out, exhaustedly, trying to fathom the amount of people — children! — my abuelito corrupted, knowing I may never fully understand the scope of his abuse.

I questioned the details further. "Your brothers were never home when your father would make you watch them have sex?" I asked in disbelief.

"At nighttime? They were probably in bed. He would just say: 'Go to the backyard' and we would go. Maybe on occasion my brothers did see. I don't know. I mean, the man was really screwed up." She paused and we sat with the fact.

"What I am going to read now is closer to what people describe as an out-of-body experience."

I prayed for this to stop. From the time I was little, about age eight, I would sleep with a rosary under my pillow because I felt my father could not hurt me since I had God so close. That night, when I lay awake in the middle of a queen size bed, I felt something tickling me on my back through the mattress. It was not a nice tickle, but a tickling that made me cry because it hurt so much. I felt it was an evil spirit, and I still believe that to this day. It was there and I felt it. At that moment I ran into my parents' room but they were both lying on the bed asleep. I was afraid of waking them up, so, crying and scared, I went back to my bedroom.

Another time I heard a noise from underneath my bed. I was so scared I stood up on my bed and jumped to the door, and ran to my parents' room which was next to mine. When I got to their room I tried to explain but they just got angry and screamed at me, telling me to go back to my room. I had this episode and they just sent me back to my room. There was never a comforting moment from my parents. It just did not exist.

I can recall bribing my two younger brothers with small toys in order to sleep in my bedroom. I would have them take turns sleeping in my room. I knew if they were there, my father would not come in. When everyone was asleep not listening, I would try locking my door, but turns out my father was rarely asleep and he would usually hear

the lock and scream at me from his room. He was always listening.
He would scream and say he wanted me to leave the door open. I
would get very upset because my mother would not say anything.

My mom's beautiful light brown eyes became watery, and her voice shaky: "It would really bother me, because my mom never defended me, and said: 'Hey, let her lock the door,' or anything of the sort. I was demanded to keep my door open. That's just the way it was."
She shrugged her shoulders and forced herself to keep reading.

From the time I was little, I recall him telling me how stupid I was.
He would hit me with his hand and whip me with a belt. I
remember going to elementary school and being embarrassed because I
had bruises all over my legs.

In a mix of exasperation and a heavy heart, she looked up at me and revealed: "He frequently grabbed a belt and whipped me! There were marks all over my legs. My teachers did nothing! Neither did the principal, or any other adult for that matter. Yet, there were whip marks all over my body." She was rightfully furious.
"It's not like the teachers couldn't see the marks on my body. I would wear dresses and you could clearly see the bruises on my legs. It was more socially accepted for kids to be spanked back then, I guess. Although, normally a spanking is on the butt."
"Not a single adult ever asked you about the bruises?" I asked, feeling her despair and desperately wanting a different answer.
"No," she said definitively. Her anger was building, her eyes narrowed, and her brow furrowed.

I thought of these adults at my mom's school who ignored the marks on her body. Why? Why did they not do anything to help this little girl? Was it because they were afraid of the truth they would encounter? Was it because physical abuse was common and practically accepted? Or was it because she was Mexican? As a first-generation Mexican American, in a rapidly changing country, she was the target of a lot of racism from a young age. At seven years old, she was forced to braid one side of her hair while her teacher forcibly braided the other in front of the class, because, according to this narrow-minded teacher who constantly accused my mom of cheating: "That is the way someone like you, Esperanza, is supposed to wear her hair."

Thinking of the layer of suffering racism added to my mom's trauma had me spinning in anguish, cycling through the incidents of cruelty and injustice in my family's history. Discrimination is not new to me. I am a brown Mexican American female, and in this world, the darker your skin the harder your journey. My parent's, and even my older sister, protected me from racism throughout my upbringing. They fought my battles for me before I even knew or understood what I was being subjected to, and before I knew how to use my own voice. But as much as I wanted to sink my anger and blame into racism, I knew it was not the only reason these adults did nothing to help my mother as a little girl.

They resisted getting involved out of fear of confronting an unimaginable truth — a truth where a little girl was viciously abused and molested by her father. I felt worn, as if I had just been beaten up. I wanted desperately to erase my abuelito from this universe, without compromising our family tree. I wanted to replace his rotten soul with pure love. Only with an abundance of love could the course of his children's and grandchildren's lives be diverted from the immense suffering already endured.

6

I can recall my father molesting three other people and peeping on one other person from when I was small. One of my friends, Michelle, was sleeping over and I wanted to sleep in my bedroom, but my father would not let us. He said we had to sleep in the living room. I've always had trouble sleeping. I guess I never felt secure as a child. I was always scared of what was going to happen next. That night, my friend and I slept on the floor, and my father came into the living room at a later hour. He kneeled next to my friend and I told him to leave. I was very upset. He slapped me in the face and told me to, 'Shut up and turn around!' I was so scared of him. When he left, she said something, and I realized she was awake and scared. She, nor any of my friends I grew up with, ever stayed the night again. They would come over less. I felt very lonely, but we always played outside.

Hearing my mom say how lonely she felt as a child made my heart sink in agony. A vision of her as a little girl flashed through my mind. She appeared, standing in the middle of a dark space, her curlicues draping past her shoulders, her head slightly tilted down, her big brown eyes gazing up in despair, a stuffed animal and rosary in her hands. She's scared. I see her surrounded by other happy little girls. Slowly, the girls fade, and my mom is left alone, in the middle of this black matter of a home, flames encroaching. I'm floating in a dark space too, screaming at the top of my lungs, with no sound to be heard. Reaching my hands out in desperation, I'm unable to reach her, pulled further away into darkness.

I tried not to cry, but there was no stopping the pain pouring from my heart, flooding my eyes.

"My friends no longer stayed the night, which was actually great for them, but as a kid you do *not* realize it's a good thing." My mom shrugged her shoulders and went back to her journal.

The second person I remember he molested was a close friend of the family, Susana. We were asleep in my room. I was so terrified of my father that his presence alone would wake me up. When I opened my eyes, he was bent over her, pulling her panties down. I told him to leave and he hit me and told me to 'Shut up.' He made me turn around and look the other way. The next morning when she woke up, she said, 'O! My underwear is down. I wonder how that happened?'

"She didn't wake up?!" I asked stupidly.
"She was pretending. Susana was staying with us for a week to help me keep the house in order after my mom had surgery. We were in junior high."
My stomach dropped learning about yet another young girl being terrorized and abused by this grown man. A man who shared my blood. A man without whom I would not exist. My mom resumed reading.

The third person I recall he molested was a cousin of mine, and that molestation took place in my bedroom in a similar way as the other. This other time, in eighth grade, I made a new friend. She became a very good friend of the family, and one day she stayed the night. The next morning, she took a shower and a while later my mom called me over and told me to tell my friend to lock the door when taking a shower because my father accidentally walked in. My friend assured

*me she locked the door, but my father must have opened it with a
key and my mom found him peeping.*

She lifted her head and raised her eyebrows. "Peeping was something
he did a lot."

I shook my head in disapproval and disgust. We went on flipping
through pictures and soon came across one of my mom's cousin Jasmine.

Tía Jasmine was the first person my mom and I spoke to once we
decided to write this book. Her openness and honesty were guiding lights
for the rest of our conversations. Being born a female in the Madero family
came with damning consequences for many, as it did for Tía Jasmine, who
was also abused. She, like many others, was more than willing to discuss
her experience with my mom and me. She had harnessed the power of
dialogue and speaking out, and she was ready to share with us. Together as
three, we gathered for a conversation that would stay with me forever.

"What do you remember most about your childhood?" I asked Tía
Jasmine while we walked around the neighborhood where she and my
mom grew up just a few houses down from one another.

"Our families," she said with a big smile on her face. "We always got
together. We did everything together. Not until everyone started getting
older and having their own kids did things start to drift a little bit, but even
then, we would find the time to gather."

We suddenly stopped walking as my tía recognized my mom's old
home.

"This is it," she said.

I looked up at the garage I had only imagined in my head for years, its
giant door like a vault to a bygone crime scene.

"How long, if you don't mind me asking, did the incidents in the 'bad
garage' go on for?" I asked.

We started referring to the garage where she, my mom, and others were
molested as the "bad garage."

"I do not know, mija. I really do not know."

My mom and Tía Jasmine went on discussing how beautiful it was to
be so close to family, despite my abuelito. They infused the moments in
between the heaviness with light chatter, and when I found a pocket of
pause, I injected us back into the heaviness.

"Is it still the original garage?" I asked, staring at its ominous door.

"Yeah, it looks like it," said Tía Jasmine gloomily.

According to both of them, the "bad garage" used to be set up with a table and a long light hanging directly above. My mom and Tía Jasmine were forced to lay on this table as young girls, the light blurring their view of Abuelito Hector standing over them as he pulled his pants down. They would cringe and cry while he violated them, robbing these sweet girls of their innocence.

Tía Jasmine's face slowly sunk into sadness. "None of us said anything. Maybe if we had, it would have stopped. We all knew not to get close to him. What bothers me though, is I cannot remember everything. I can bring certain images to mind, but I have always been unsure of how far it went."

I listened to them, immobile, my skin crawling with discomfort, my eyes, with theirs, focused on the "bad garage."

My tía interrupted our speechlessness with a smile and relieving affirmation: "Families have to stick together! Help each other in good times and bad. This was not our fault! Especially my prima here. I do not know how she survived."

They embraced one another, exchanging empathy and love with an elongated hug. They pulled away and my mom broke the silence.

"Earlier we were talking about Tío Oscar…"

Tía Jasmine interjected immediately: "Wow… I almost didn't say anything about him — in case you didn't know!"

The instinct to stay quiet about abuse is a strong one, and remained strong among my mom and her cousin even as we delved openly into the topic. I knew about Tío Oscar — a close relative of Abuelito Hector's — and his abusive ways well before starting this book, so I was expecting his name to come up eventually. Unfortunately, there was more than one monster in these women's lives as children, though Tío Oscar's evil could not compare to Abuelito Hector's.

Tía Jasmine continued, "Tío Oscar was the same way as Tío Hector. He used to work at the drive-through dairy, and when I walked there with our boy cousins, Tío Oscar would wait until they weren't looking and just… pull it out right in front of me, wanting me to touch him.

"When I think of the abuse, sometimes I see Tío Hector's face and sometimes I see Tío Oscar's. I do not know how many times it happened. The strange part is… I do not hate your dad," she said looking at my mom.

"It is not to say it is not his fault, but I know something happened to him and he needed help and did not get it. I mean, aside from the bad things your dad did, he always seemed nice. He was nice up until…"

She could not find the right words for a statement that contradicted itself.

"Maybe there was something…" she trailed off.

"Something that flipped," my mom said in a distant tone.

We stood silently, our heads tilted as we stared at the "bad garage," our bodies drenched in the warm rays of yellow sunshine, filling us with the bright light we needed.

My mom turned her gaze towards me. "Did he ever molest you?" She somehow asked me casually, as she had done several times throughout my life, giving me the chance to speak up in case I was still holding onto a dark secret. My mom and Tía Jasmine stared at me for what seemed like light-years. I felt like a little girl looking up at them looming over me, as if they were ten feet tall. Their eyes bulged lovingly at me, as my shoulders tensed up to my ears, showing how awkward I felt inside.

"No," I said, trying to match my mom's nonchalance, but feeling angst in my body, and tightness in my chest and throat. "Not that I remember. But I have always been prepared for the worst in case of a flashback."

My mom and Tía Jasmine stood still, another light-year passing as their eyes gently centered on me. The sound of my own breathing roared in my ears. My eyes bounced back and forth between them, as I figured out what to say next.

"But no, not that I remember. At this point, if I were to remember something, I would be ready to accept it. At least I hope." I knew other individuals whose brains suppressed memories of sexual trauma, only to have them come back decades later completely unexpectedly, triggered by the tiniest of connections to the past. I had seen the shock that can take over one's life with that kind of revelation. Deep down inside, I don't think Abuelito Hector ever touched me inappropriately, but every now and then I question my confidence in that reality. The doubts that linger push me to prepare myself for any truth… just in case.

They both nodded with sounds of affirmation, still staring at me. They waited patiently for anything else I may need to say. I smiled nervously and laughed with my lips tightly locked. We all sighed, and my mom broke the uneasy quiet for me.

"When something like this happens, you think it's your own fault," my mom said sternly, her eyes sad and brown like a worn-out teddy bear's.

"You feel as if you are the one who did something wrong. Like if you say something…"

"Then you are the dirty one," Tía Jasmine finished.

I jumped into the conversation, "When abused as a kid, sometimes these feelings arrive that push you towards a mental struggle of: 'Did I like it? Did I not?' and that confusion comes from being forced at such a young age into sexual activity before you're ready. Those thoughts alone can make you feel guilt and shame all over again. Many straight men abused as kids are forced to contemplate: 'Am I gay? Am I not?' stemming from a forced sexual experience by an older male."

They nodded in agreement.

My mom let out a heavy sigh and reflected, "It's difficult, right?"

We did not answer right away, leaving a pocket of silence ringing in our ears before Tía Jasmine declared, "Yeah. But, sometimes it takes somebody else speaking up for you to say, 'me too.'"

We all agreed, having experienced or witnessed this effect first-hand and seen it ripple through our family. Acknowledgment of the truth is contagious.

Despite the dark forces against us, being in the presence of these women gave me new strength to take on the world in the face of catastrophe. I welcomed the heat of the sun sinking into my body, cementing me to the ground. This was my first interview, and I pulled all the courage and inspiration I could from it in order to continue. I smiled at the armageddon that was, empowered by the women who came before me to speak the truth loudly.

Tía Jasmine turned to face my mom and me, "But hey, we had a lot of great times." Her eyes sparkled with a semblance of lasting innocence.

"We did indeed!" echoed my mom with a big grin on her face.

The two cousins beamed with nostalgia and gratitude for one another. Their infectious laughter wrapped around me like a blanket of encouragement as I watched and listened to these two beautiful women, who had just dove into the darkest depths of their abyss, relish in the sweetness of life.

7

I knew writing this book would be exceptionally challenging, and in 2013, my life's course proved I was not yet ready. Life — work, mental states, obligations of all kinds —had pulled my mom and I away from writing this book for five years. In the spring of 2018, it brought us back. Thanks to an Ayahuasca ceremony of mine, and the decent chunk of savings I'd mustered over the years, I set off on a quest that I was meant for all along. I quit my job and dedicated myself solely to this book. My hunger to explore my family's story further had not abated. And so, we saddled up yet again, and I met with several more of my mom's cousins and friends, seeking their raw accounts from the blazing labyrinth of childhood sexual trauma and my abuelito's murky hell. I started with Tía Elsa, my mom's first cousin.

My Tía Elsa is tall, with light brown curly hair, thin sharply drawn eyebrows, and a deadpan expression that breaks with her constant laughter. She is a straight shooter, and I have always admired that in her. She used to be quite intimidating in her day, considered a "sassy chola" many people were afraid of. We've laughed about that many times together — she may be blunt, but her nature is unmistakably loving. We relaxed on a park bench while she shared some of her hard truths with me.

"When I was in my mid-teens, we were at your grandparents' house visiting, and all the adults were in the add-on your grandpa built in the backyard. I think he purposely built the additional room so nobody would know what was going on in the house. Anyways, my cousin Roberto and I were walking down the hall when your grandpa got out of the shower and called to us, wearing only a towel: 'Roberto, come here, Roberto!' Roberto froze and slightly shook his head 'no.' Next thing we know, your grandpa dropped his towel and his private part was hard. He just stared at us smiling and we ran."

Another horrifying memory popped into her head. "When your mom and I were younger, I would spend the night with her, and we always slept in the living room. It was fun to be together, but… I woke up once and your grandpa was on top of me. He was touching me. He put his hand over my mouth so nobody could hear me scream. As a kid, you are frightened, and where do you run? Your parents are not there, and the adults who are supposed to be taking care of you are the ones abusing you. Somebody once said your grandpa was like a dog, and I said, 'No, he is not like a dog. Dogs are beautiful, loyal, and they take care of their young. He is not even a dog.' I don't have a name for him."

The families spent almost every weekend and holiday together, usually ending up at Carmen and Hector's house. They were the lovey-dovey couple, enamored with each other and life. Nobody expected such horrendous and irreparable acts from them. Their sins got lost in everyone's profound respect and adoration for them. People looked up to them. Their community looked up to them — they were, after all, the big brother and big sister of their families. With Hector's penchant for alcohol and loud music, and Carmen making tortillas daily by hand and bean tacos that made your mouth water with the scent alone, the Madero home was where family and friends wanted to be.

Next in line to meet with were my Tía Sara and Tía Erica, who were practically sisters — little cousins to my mom and attached at the hip as kids — but I wanted to speak with them separately. The stories they each shared took place between the ages of six and eight years old, making my mom somewhere between eleven and thirteen. I met with Tía Erica first.

Tía Erica is a pensive, yet speedy conversationalist with a soothing voice. Her presence calms you and her openness earns your trust. She has a big smile and kind brown eyes. I picked her up one rainy evening in Huntington Beach, we grabbed tea from a cafe, and settled in the car in the parking lot. She began sharing stories against the backdrop of light rain falling on the windshield.

"Your tía Sara and I were close — we still are — and we would walk in a pair, at least whenever he was around, which was almost always. I vividly remember one New Year's Eve when we all spent the night at your grandparents' house. I was in your grandparents' bedroom. I don't know how I got there, I just remember being there. I don't remember being touched or any kind of penetration. It was more of me having to touch him. There was a mirrored wardrobe and I saw everything through the mirror. I can still see it happening."

She said this with a seriousness that cemented me to my seat. She remained in contemplative stillness for a few seconds before looking up at me.

"I don't know if it was that same day or a different one, but there was a bathroom in the hallway, and, I don't know if that is where... because..." She stopped to breathe and collect her thoughts. I recalled other people sharing stories of walking down this exact hallway to the bathroom. It played out in my head like a scary movie, slowly walking down the narrow, dimly lit hall, the quiet swallowing my surroundings, my heartbeat vibrating through my entire body.

I lifted my eyes to meet Tía Erica's. Flashes of fragmented memories seemed to flood her mind. The rhythm of her speech quickened as she pulled the memories out, ordering them into a story in front of us.

"Blue. The bathroom was blue. Maybe that is where I was when your grandpa brought me into their bedroom...or maybe that was a different occasion. I just remember being in that bathroom with him. We tried to avoid the hallway bathroom when we could. We went instead to the bathroom by the kitchen because it was in an open space, but it wasn't always empty. If you were in the hallway bathroom... you know what I mean?"

She gave me a look while shrugging her shoulders. I knew. She knew I knew. She gulped another big breath and continued.

"I was always looking out for Alicia, you know?" I did. Alicia was her younger sister. "One time we were at my parent's house, and thankfully Tía Sara and I saw your grandpa follow Alicia outside, so we went out after her. Nothing happened, thankfully. He just tried to do this to her pants," she imitated Abuelito Hector pulling the top of her sister's pants out to look down at her underwear. "We got out there and immediately brought her back inside."

The thought of a child so young at such great risk of harm haunted me.

"I do not remember ever talking about it," Tía Erica said. "We never really said anything to anybody. He never said, 'Don't tell anybody.' It was simply not discussed — not even as kids. Ever. I just remember growing up and feeling creepy about it all. Your tía Sara and I would say to each other, 'He's creepy and nasty. Watch out,' but we never told anybody about what he did to us. We just knew to watch out for each other."

Despite the terror and panic these stories evoke, I could not help but feel bursts of a fiery strength. I smiled at Tía Erica and breathed in her courage.

The following day I met with Tía Sara, who has a strong brow and even stronger nose, and thin lips that display her perfectly straight teeth. Of all my mom's cousins, Tía Sara has the greatest sense of humor. Her laughter and constant joking bring levity and fun to every room she walks into, but on this day, we came together to discuss the dark topic of sexual abuse.

We met at my parents' house in the late afternoon, just the two of us, and made ourselves comfortable on the living room sofa. She initiated the conversation the only way she knew how — by cracking jokes.

"So, when are we getting the party started?" she said with a smirk. "Are the strippers hiding in the closet?" We both laughed before centering ourselves for the conversation we knew was waiting for us.

"What I remember most is the mirror your grandpa put up in the living room. That mirror..." she said, shaking her head. "I always wondered how he knew when I was going to the bathroom, until one day, I realized he strategically placed the mirror so that when he stood at the bar, he could see all the way down the hall to the bathroom. I would be in there..." she trailed off before continuing.

"He would be so close behind that he would just come in. He would pull his pants down and put my hand on the crown of his penis, forcing me to touch him," she said in a low and disturbed tone. "He never touched my privates. It was me having to touch him. Then the kissing."

She made annoyed sounds while rolling her eyes and shaking her head.

"That damn mirror," she said again. "It was traumatizing just to see it. I always went to the bathroom with your tía Erica so we wouldn't be alone. Still, we were not safe. We were both forced to touch him. Sometimes I would avoid going to the bathroom all together at their house. If he was at the bar, I would hold my pee or crawl to the bathroom. I was terrified!" She chuckled through the torment. "I'm lucky I was not one of his main targets. I'm lucky he didn't do more to me, like what he did to others. Like what he did to your mom," she said mournfully.

I was moved by her courage and intrigued to hear her minimize her experience. What Abuelito Hector did to her was something no child should ever go through. No matter what he did to others, her experience was traumatic, and I was here to give it the space it deserved. Humans are notorious for minimizing and deflecting their own pain and suffering. The more survivors I spoke with and the more I reflected, the more I saw this trend, as if it were a tool to make sense of what happened to them and be thankful for what didn't.

"When I would say 'Hi' to greet him and give him a hug and kiss on the cheek, he would turn to get a kiss on the lips. He would also make us sit on his lap." Her face showed disgust. "I don't know if that was so he could feel us on him, but as a child your mind does not go there. As I got older, I realized how gross it was. I always tried to hide or keep my distance from him, because I was terribly afraid of him. He knew we were not going to say anything, because as young children, you just don't.

"Growing up, my parents always told my siblings and I: 'If anybody ever touches you, you tell us,' but they never explained what kind of touching was bad. They also didn't consistently ask if anyone ever touched us, which is a conversation that needs to stay open with children. The damages of sexual abuse stay with you and hinder your emotional stability. That is the hard part. You are so young that you become completely confused. I don't recall how many times this happened to me, but I never told anybody. I stayed quiet. It was embarrassing and I thought I would get in trouble. At such a young age, you don't know that you shouldn't be embarrassed, or that it is not your fault."

I quickly came to understand that it was not enough to rely on a child to tell you if anyone ever touches them. Even if you consistently ask them to tell you. As adults, we need to take the responsibility of diving deeper into these conversations with our children.

Soon after, my mom reached out to two of her closest childhood friends about sharing their uncomfortable experiences with her father, and they agreed.

We awaited their 5 p.m. arrival nervously. The women's cars pulled up to my parents' house, and I felt an immediate sense of excitement. I have always loved being around my mom's friend Michelle. Her energy is vivacious, kind, yet very direct and always comedic. I had not seen her in years, and was delighted when she walked through the door, lovely as ever. She quickly began joking at every turn, regardless of the heaviness at hand.

April was quieter, and exceptionally warm, with her light blue eyes and short blonde bob. I remembered April, but not as vividly as Michelle. Her presence was soft and timid, unless you gave her the space to open up, which is exactly what we did. We made our way to the kitchen, served ourselves dinner, and assembled at the dining room table to begin the delicate, but long-overdue conversation.

"Everybody was always over at the Madero home," recalled April. "There was always a pot of something on the stove."

"Oh yes, there was always a party," said Michelle. She looked up and locked eyes with me. "We have never spoken to your mom about this. We discuss it," she said, pointing to herself and April, "but never with your mom." She turned to my mom with a smile and said: "So, Esperanza, you need to go outside. Sorry!"

We all laughed, and my mom questioned: "Are you sure you're comfortable with me here?"

"Oh totally!" replied April.

"Of course! I'm just joking!" snapped Michelle in a refreshingly sassy, yet loving manner.

My mom was always intentional about creating a safe, open environment to share these ruthless stories. "I'm just making sure. I don't want to make anyone uncomfortable. Please, do *not* feel like you need to hold back because I'm here. Say everything and be honest. If you want to say something that is not nice, please just say it." I smiled at my mother's innocuousness.

We caught up about our lives, until I found the right opening to switch gears. "What were your experiences with my mom's family and her parents? Anything weird?"

"A lot weird!" said April, before cooling down the soup on her spoon. "We would be in the kitchen, and he would come in and suck on my nose," April said firmly.

"He would what?!" my mom asked in shock.

"Suck on my nose," April stated again, even more firmly.

"Suck on your nose?!" my mom repeated in utter dismay.

"In front of everybody," stated April. "I would stand there, and you know… the kitchen was always full of people."

"That is so gross," said my mom. "The weird part is, the more stories I hear, the more I realize his mind was even more twisted than I thought. It's sick. Everything he did is sick, but it's…" She was still baffled at how much her father was able to get away with.

Michelle jumped in. "He would kiss me and stick his tongue down my mouth. When I would come over to the house — and I was there almost every day — that's how he would greet me. I would try and avoid him by entering the house through the side door or through the boys' room in the garage."

"He would stick his tongue in my ears!" April exclaimed. "I would freeze up."

Somehow, after all these stories, I was still utterly shocked by these ones.

My mom picked up where April left off: "Then you don't want to say anything to anyone, because you feel like you are the one doing something wrong, and you're not, but you feel like you are."

"You start to wonder, is this happening to everybody else? Is this just normal life?" Michelle asked, somewhat rhetorically.

"In our case," said April, referring to herself and Michelle, "neither one of us had a dad at home, so we really did not know how dads were."

Michelle added, "Hector was one of the main dads of the neighborhood, and he manipulated many of us."

My soul yearned for them as children, for all the children he manipulated.

Michelle turned to look at my mom: "Esperanza, I saw him with you. Did I ever tell you?" she asked anxiously.

"No, you didn't," my mom responded, eager to hear what Michelle had seen.

"It may have been twice, now that I'm remembering. We must have been in middle school. I walked into your house looking for you. I went down the hallway to go into your room and walked by your parents' bedroom. The door was slightly open, and I saw him on top of you. I don't remember if you both had clothes on or not, but I ran out of the house. I was furious, questioning why nobody was doing anything about this, and why I had to be the one to see. I just remember him being on top of you and I was freaking out."

My mom reached over and grabbed Michelle's hand: "The crazy part is, he did not always try to hide what he did. A lot of it was right in front of other people. He knew how to hide it in plain sight."

April chimed in: "He felt wildly superior. Like: 'You can't touch me.'"

The irony. We remained still for several seconds, taking it all in, letting our bodies feel the disturbance of anger and absurdity in full. Still, we stayed grounded in our cumulative strength and gratitude for the present.

Michelle started again. "You always used to beg us to spend the night. Remember, Esperanza?"

"Yeah! Because I was terrified of my dad," she declared, laughing.

Michelle smiled at her, "You would stand by your bedroom door and beg us to stay, and we'd apologetically say, 'No, no, no! We don't want to spend the night!' or, 'My mom won't let me.' You would tear up, but we never communicated the truth of why we didn't want to stay."

My mom interjected: "I felt like nobody loved me or liked me, because nobody wanted to stay the night. Looking back, of course nobody wanted to stay the night."

We all smiled as Michelle went ahead. "When we did spend the night, we would usually sleep in the living room. We would hold the blankets up so tight trying to keep his hands out. One time he came and laid on top of me..." Michelle let her words hang in suspension while we stared at her with our jaws dropped.

Michelle matched our silent shock with a resounding: "Yep!" and pursed her lips while nodding her head. "I was lying with my stomach on the floor, and he laid on top of me. On a separate occasion I was laying there, and he walked into the kitchen, naked."

April interjected: "That same night, he touched my butt and also laid on top of me. I think he was naked. Again, I was frozen. Frozen! He put his hands down my pajama pants... but only once that I recall. I was so scared. But we were not there every night, so it was not ongoing for us."

My mom confirmed, "You cannot scream, you cannot talk, you cannot do anything. You are robbed of your ability to do anything other than freeze."

April nodded in agreement. "Freezing up is the worst part. That feeling is what I remember most. What has stuck with me the most."

Thirteen women and four men. Seventeen people total. That is the number of family and friends I spoke to for this book, and each of their voices are spread throughout in unique ways. These women and men are the unsung heroes of this story, and there are so many more just like them. They are the heroes who broke their silence.

This journey has allowed me to surrender to a part of my family history I have long shut out, falling back into the infinite darkness to investigate life's great abominations. The beauty is, the deeper I go, the stronger I become, the further I grow into the power of my light, and the more I learn how to stand up to dark forces and fill the void with love. I could not have explored so deeply nor relinquished controls so fully, without the courage of each woman and each man so willing to speak out.

8

It was the winter of 1973, and on Esperanza's twelfth birthday, she woke up like most kids do, excited to celebrate with her family and friends. Soon after opening her eyes and stretching, her mother burst into her room: "Hey! Get up! I need you to come do some house work." Esperanza was instantly deflated, saddened her mother left her room without saying the magic words she so desperately wanted to hear that morning. She dragged herself out of bed, got dressed, and began her chores, like she had done from the age of five.

While Esperanza mopped the floor, Michelle and April came bouncing in with huge smiles on their faces, singing, "Happy Birthday to you! Happy Birthday to you!" Esperanza's joy and delight in seeing them quickly turned to fear.

"Shhh! Quiet, quiet, quiet!" she whispered.

"What's wrong?!" asked Michelle and April in unison.

"I think my parents forgot my birthday. My mom put me to work the second I got up and never even said happy birthday to me." Michelle's and April's faces dropped in disbelief, sad for their friend and angry at her parents.

Michelle and April hung around, keeping their friend company with small talk until she was done cleaning. Then, the three girls ran out of the house, giggling and hugging, ready to celebrate Esperanza's birthday together. It was friends like these who created sudden bursts of bliss in a life otherwise brimming with terror and abuse. Esperanza's relationships with her friends, cousins, and brothers were her anchor to the world, along with her strong faith in God, helping her stay alive.

It was clear, Esperanza's parents' neglect knew no bounds and it stung Esperanza like fire. She barely had time to heal before the next scorching flame came around — a never ending fire.

In the few years that followed, Esperanza got her period, developed breasts, experienced her first crush, and deepened her friendships. The abuse continued throughout. Away from her father, however, she could allow herself to fully enjoy the present.

In the fall of 1976, a 14-year-old Esperanza entered high school, and like many of her peers, Esperanza was thrilled about her first homecoming dance. She knew, however, that her father would be a major obstacle.

She pleaded.

"Please?! Please let me go to the dance, Dad?!" He looked at her with an evil smirk, preparing his ultimatum. "Okay," he replied. "In exchange for a sexual favor." Esperanza's body tensed up, knowing she would have to play his dirty game.

"Okay. I'll do it. But only after the dance. That way I know you'll let me go."

Hector eyed her with a villainous stare. "Fine. But you have to hold up your end of the deal the night after the dance."

Esperanza nodded her head reluctantly. She knew getting out of this arrangement would be arduous. As shocking and horrifying as it was, Esperanza was used to this kind of degradation. She had been battling with her father's demons for over a decade and was naturally training for her eventual escape. All she cared about was that she could attend the dance with her friends and have a normal teenage night — and that she did.

The night after the homecoming dance, Hector waited for his family to fall asleep before barging into his daughter's room.

"Esperanza, it's time to fulfill your agreement," he said sternly.

Angry and full of resentment, Esperanza resisted. "No! No! I won't do it!" She was older now and finding her voice. She was also big enough now to try and fight him off, and fight she did. Hector grew indignant, launching himself towards his daughter, trying to hit her, but she jumped out of the way. She was the faster mouse to his aging cat, a game Hector had been forcing her to play for years.

Esperanza started raising her voice to alarm her brothers, and finally her father backed down. He scurried out of her room angrily, and while she was safe for now, she knew she would not get off so easily. Soon enough, the beatings intensified. And to, quite literally, add insult to injury, Hector stopped talking to his daughter for months at a time, unless other people were around and he was forced to. Otherwise, she did not exist, deepening Esperanza's pain.

Silent treatment from her father, her relentless predator, would seem like a blessing, but it just made Esperanza feel more belittled. Not only was her abuse invisible, now she was, too. Her father found a new way to diminish her self worth. Their relationship may have been a torturous one, but she still craved the familial normalcy she saw her friends and cousins — even her brothers — enjoy with their dads. She continued to hold out hope for a caring, loving father.

Soon thereafter, Esperanza's moment of normalcy finally arrived. It was the day many soon to be 15-year-old Mexican girls dream about. Adorned in her lacey, white, poofy dress, surrounded by her family and friends she loved so dearly, Esperanza celebrated her quinceañera. The sun provided a beautiful warm day for Esperanza and her guests to revel in her symbolic transition from girlhood to womanhood. She felt like a princess as her brothers and parents showered her with praise, adoration, and affection — acts of love not uncommon from her brothers, but unquestionably bizarre from her parents. She was, nonetheless, overjoyed by her father's thoughtful and warm demeanor that day, her happiest in life so far. While she couldn't understand what brought on his sudden attitude shift, she decided to enjoy it rather than question it. It was her day and she openly accepted all the love.

When my mom initially began sharing detailed stories with me about her life in 2013, Abuelito Hector was alive. As we sat in the car parked across the school that first day, we leafed through photos until she spotted one that agitated her.

"There I am in a bathing suit with Abuelita Elena," my mom said, pointing. "I was fifteen. My father unexpectedly took a picture of us and I was incredibly bothered. He ended up putting the original on his nightstand next to where he slept. Me and Abuelita Elena in bathing suits. He probably still has it," she said with rightful contempt.

Our irritated faces and furrowed brows told the story of two women disturbed, searching for clarity but coming up dry. I gently bit the inside of my mouth. My mom shook her head.

"I was really uncomfortable the day I went to buy that bikini because my father insisted on looking at every one I tried on. It was the only two piece I ever bought. I always felt very uncomfortable exposing my body."

I rubbed my forehead in dismay. "Nobody noticed there was a picture of you in a bikini on his nightstand?" I asked.

"I don't know. It was a nice picture of my abuelita and me walking next to each other. It could have been cute, but it was not, given the circumstance. I asked him to move it once, but he refused. It's a circle. You think it's going to end, and it doesn't."

My mom stared at me, making sure I was okay. I nodded my head and smiled in assurance.

"There is so much I do not have written down...like the last time he sexually abused me," she shared. I took a deep breath and braced myself for the story to come.

"A bunch of family and friends went to Central Park in Huntington Beach for a barbeque, and my good friend Susana and I took our bikes. It was shortly after my quinceañera," established my mom. "We were riding our bikes around the park when we decided to go to Jeff's house, my boyfriend at the time. He lived a couple miles away and once we got there, we hung out playing pool with his parents and two brothers. Before we knew it, nightfall arrived, and it was getting dark. Jeff's mom offered to give us a ride home, but I declined, knowing that would get us in even more trouble. We did not tell anyone where we were going, so we rode our bikes back to the park as fast as we could. When we arrived back, it was pretty dark."

My mom cleared her throat. "My father was holding a flashlight, and so was Susana's dad. They flashed the light on us as we rode up, and it wasn't until we reached them that we saw how angry they were. My dad started yelling and moving closer, until he reached me and began furiously hitting me on the head with his flashlight. It's a miracle he didn't knock me out."

She paused, allowing my shock to absorb, and shrugged her shoulders, as if to say *that's just the way he was*, before jumping back into her story.

"A random guy on a skateboard rode by and my dad thought he was connected to me somehow, so he started calling me a whore. My friend's dad was about to hit her too, but she glared at him and in a stern voice said, 'Don't you dare, Dad,' and he backed down. I was hoping that would encourage my father to back down too, but he didn't. He continued beating me. After he stopped, I plopped down crying, and your dad was actually there. He had a crush on me and any time he knew we were going to the park, he would go. On that day, he found me crying."

We both chuckled a bit, pulling the silver lining out of this horrible story — the silver lining of a young love that would soon blossom and eventually grow a family tree.

"I cried all night, and the next day my father came into my room and started hitting me again and calling me names."

My mom described their exchange:

"No, Dad, I didn't do anything!" Esperanza shouted.

"Yes, you did! I saw the guy take off on his skateboard! You whore!" he roared.

"No! I don't even know who he was! We biked over to Jeff's house and were playing pool with him and his family! His parents were there, too!" She hoped the truth would set her free.

"No! I don't believe you! You were having sex! Let me check you!" he demanded angrily.

"No! No! Please, Dad, no!"

"If you don't let me check you, I am going to take you to the doctor and have *him* check you!"

"Okay, fine! Let's go to the doctor. Let's have him check me!" Her voice exuded strength, challenging him, knowing she did nothing wrong. Yet the oppression embroiled in a virginity check was lost on both of them.

"I cannot believe you are going to let somebody else touch you!" he screamed furiously, as if she were breaking a romantic covenant. He hit her some more, before "checking" her himself, shoving his hands inside her forcefully while she sobbed.

"Take me to Fernando's! I want to go to Fernando's!" she cried out after he finished his dirty work, seeking the protection of her oldest brother.

"No, no!" he pleaded with her, suddenly frightened of what would happen if the truth got out. "I will take you wherever you want. Your boyfriend's house, a friend's house, anywhere but Fernando's!"

"No! I want to talk to Fernando. Take me to his house!" she cried.

"No, please! Promise me you will never tell anybody. I will take you to your boyfriend's house if you want!" he pleaded.

"No! Take me to Fernando's house now!" she yelled back.

She did not remember if her father took her to Fernando's or not, but she knew she never told her brother what happened that day. It was, however, the last time he laid hands on her sexually — though not physically.

My body struggled through the retelling of this violent story. The thought of Abuelito Hector "checking" my mom's body was incredibly sickening and chilled me to my core. I focused on my breathing to stay calm so I could ask my mom the questions that would help her unpack.

She began describing her father's unhealthy relationship with alcohol. "He was an everyday drinker, although he was not a fall-down drunk. His bar was stocked with all kinds of liquor, and he constantly had a glass in his hand. He was abusive, but directed his violence to a select few, mainly young girls. A couple months after the last time he sexually abused me, we were in the family room, just the two of us. He was taking shots of hard liquor and saying really mean remarks to me. I was crying and in a desperate attempt said, 'Dad, I would really like it if you stopped drinking and would change your ways with me.' He looked right at me, laughed, and pounded the remaining liquor in his glass. He did it just to spite me."

Silence rang louder than a thousand screams in my mom's car that day. A sharpness shot through my ears and I felt my body go numb. I felt weightless, as if I was lifted out of my seat, staring into the void of my shell-shocked brain. For the first time ever, I was having a hard time accepting that he was my abuelito, that I shared his blood. I felt myself spiral, spinning further and further away from myself.

There were still many truths I could not comprehend, like how all of this abuse could have remained hidden for so long. I reignited my quest for answers and started calculating ages. The last time my mom was molested by her father she was 15, making her three younger brothers 14, 10, and 9 years old. They were young kids themselves. My mom sketched the layout of their house, and I realized her brothers' rooms were set away from hers and her parents'. It was starting to make sense.

In the winter of 2018, I met with Tío Leo — the fourth born in the Madero tribe of five — who was 10 the last time my mom was molested. Tío Leo is tall with kind brown eyes, stern yet humorous, and particularly forthright. He has never been known to hold back his thoughts. He is one of my mother's best friends. We gathered just the two of us in his living room to discuss the fiery subject.

I am close to my tío, but this was the first time we spoke together about the offenses committed by his father, my abuelito. This was the first time we met to examine just how gravely his parent's actions affected our family. He started by acknowledging the normalcy of his childhood.

"My mom was nurturing, and my dad was a good provider. He spent a lot of time on the road as a service man when I was growing up, which meant he was gone a lot. The times he was around, he went out of his way to take us places. We went camping, and we got together with family a lot. I don't know that "hero" is the right word for how I saw him then, but he was my dad, and growing up, you only have your dad as a reference point of what a man is. I knew no different. That was the norm for me. Nothing seemed too out of place."

It is interesting how people living under the same roof, sharing many of the same daily adventures, end up with completely different experiences and perspectives. Ultimately, we live our individual realities, and can never know what goes on behind closed doors — not even the closed doors in our own home.

While my mom was forced to trudge through the infernal abyss my abuelito created, her brothers enjoyed the right to live outside of it, in the light. Abuelito Hector was able to manipulate his own children into thinking life was normal, nothing was amiss, and everyone was happy. And so his sons believed that their sister lived in the same light.

That was not true.

Thankfully, the power of our own body, mind, and soul, allow us to be our own healers. My mom, dad, Abuelita Elena, and paternal abuelitos have shown me that no matter our afflictions, our mindset can pull us out of the depths of darkness and into infinite fresh air. While the darkness is never far from reach, we can train ourselves to love and care for this fear with softness and grace.

9

It was a pleasantly radiant day in the summer of 2018 in Huntington Beach, California. The thriving garden in my parents' backyard set a welcome juxtaposition to the dark topic my dad, Ricardo, and I were about to explore. My parents tended their garden daily with care, and it was obvious by the health and happiness of the plants. Amidst the naturally brilliant shades of greens, yellows, reds, and purples, against the aged red brick, we made ourselves comfortable in our rocking chairs and dove into the dark.

My dad was incredibly open to discussing my mom's abusive past with me. He was the most involved with her journey since she was 18, and his perspective is invaluable to the story.

His dark hair starting to thin, his bushy eyebrows greying, and his kind brown eyes recalling the past, he kicked his legs up on the firepit and rocked his chair ever so slightly. My dad's voice came beaming into the air around us, as I listened intently to the genesis of my parents' story.

❧

Ricardo had a major crush on Esperanza, and like many of Esperanza's peers, he saw her family as an inspiration. It was the beginning of 1975 when he met Esperanza for the first time. He had recently arrived to the United States, having immigrated from Mexico at 17 years young. They both lived in Huntington Beach and had mutual family friends. Ricardo's style matched the classic fashions of the era: bell-bottoms, earth-toned long-sleeve button-downs, sleek leather boots, and long wavy hair. His Mexican accent made him quite the enticing character. At 20, he spent his days working, basking in the sun, and his newfound freedom to build the life he dreamed of.

Ricardo had been thinking of a gift to give Esperanza to show his passion and fondness for her. She had another boyfriend at the time, but that did not keep Ricardo from making his feelings known. Finally, he decided on a gift that was sure to win her over. After spending weeks fixing it up, he drove it over to her house one balmy summer evening.

He was sure this Buick was the greatest gift she could receive, and he was dead set on presenting it to her in a grand display of his affinity for her. Esperanza and Daniel, her youngest brother, happened to be hanging outside when Ricardo pulled up. Esperanza, confused but curious, asked what he was doing.

"I have a present for you." Ricardo answered with a proud smile on his face and arm out the window. He tapped the side of the car and looked at Esperanza enthusiastically, "I want you to have it."

Esperanza was taken aback by such a grand gesture and thanked him profusely but assured him she did not need a car. Surprised, Ricardo stood firm: he wanted to give it to her regardless.

"Thank you, but no. I can't accept this gift. And I don't need a car," she insisted.

Daniel was even more shocked by his sister's response. He jumped up and down begging for her to accept. "Come on, sis! Take it! Just take the car!" But Esperanza's mind was made up.

Frustrated with her decline, Ricardo shot back, "Well, if you don't like this car, I'll go get you my Mustang!" Esperanza and Daniel stood in the driveway as they watched Ricardo frustratedly speed away in a hurry. Esperanza grinned while looking down at a puddle of oil that came from the Buick Ricardo supposedly had just fixed up. "That is the last man I would ever marry," Esperanza told Daniel, shaking her head and grinning at Ricardo's apparent determination. Another two years would go by before a real relationship sprouted between the two, and Ricardo never did return with that Mustang.

After speaking with my dad, I joined my mom in the dining room. A mural inspired by Purepero was painted on the largest wall behind us. She proceeded to share with me the years in between the Buick and the blossoming of her and my dad's relationship.

That "other boyfriend" Esperanza had was named Matt. They were together for a little over a year. He was told by a coworker — who happened to be the mother of one of Esperanza's best friends — that

Esperanza had a "funny" relationship with her father, and she was pretty sure he was sexually abusing her.

Seriously concerned about the girl he had mounting feelings for, Matt called Esperanza at school, on the telephone line in the student body office. She was the school treasurer and spent a considerable amount of time there, so he was confident about getting a hold of her. She picked up the line and he told her they needed to speak in private, immediately.

Thankfully, Esperanza was in the room alone. Feeling safe to unpack the sensitive topic, Matt asked Esperanza if what his co-worker told him was true. Her initial reaction was sadness that this adult clearly knew something was not right but chose not to act. This woman could have told social services or someone who could have helped Esperanza when she was younger but didn't. Nervous, but not one to lie, she confirmed that it was true. Matt consoled Esperanza, and for the first time she felt like she had a friend to lean on.

She let Matt know her father had not sexually abused her in a couple years, yet he insisted she speak with two of his best friends who happened to be pastors. The idea of opening up gave her a hint of vindication she had not felt before, and so she was happy to meet with them. From there she got the courage to confront her mother.

She was soon to be 17 and knew her mother was well aware of the abuse. One night, while her father was away on business, Esperanza decided to finally face her.

"Mom, can we talk?" Esperanza asked nervously as her mother straightened out the living room.

"About what, mija?" Carmen asked, obliviously.

"Well," her heart rate accelerated but she pressed on, "I want to know why you never did anything about Dad abusing me."

Carmen, caught off guard, instantly became stiff. "What are you talking about?" she asked anxiously, feigning ignorance.

"Well, you know Dad sexually abused me since I was a little girl. Why didn't you ever do anything about it?"

Carmen stood still, expressionless, offering only silence to her daughter.

Esperanza, growing frustrated, laid out the details for her mother, telling her about all the years of abuse, asking again why she allowed it to happen. And yet again, Carmen was silent, responding only in tears. Assured her mother would not answer, Esperanza walked away, leaving her mother crying in the living room.

Later that night when Hector made his nightly call, Carmen broke down on the phone, ending the conversation in an argument, the loud murmurs of which Esperanza could hear from the rare safety of her closed bedroom.

Days later, Hector returned from his trip and immediately bombarded Esperanza.

"Why did you bring this up to your mom? I have not done anything to you in years. Now she's mad at me!" Hector complained bitterly as he stormed away from his daughter. Esperanza was appalled and deeply saddened by her father's unfair reaction.

That is as far as the conversation went with her mother. Carmen had no idea how to handle confronting the horrors she enabled for years, so she buried it deeper into her subconscious and went on as if her daughter never said a word about it — or worse yet, as if she never witnessed it herself.

❧

Immersed in the bright colors of the Purepero mural, I stared at my mom with a flood of tears in my eyes and a smile on my face, utterly inspired.

"You are really strong," I said.

"I don't know. I'm tough in a way, I guess. I had to be strong in order to survive. I get it from Abuelita Elena. She was just a resilient woman. Her and God. God became meaningful to me early on in life. Without God I would have…" she trailed off before restarting.

"I was always scared of committing suicide because I used to believe I would go to hell, and I did not want to go to hell." Her tone shot up. "Are you kidding? I wanted to be gone so many times. Growing up I use to think, *If I just kill myself now, I won't have to go through life getting molested by my father.*"

"Did you ever try to go through with it?" I asked apprehensively.

"I planned it out several times. Thankfully I never went through with it. I was 11 years old the first time I thought about suicide. I would think of the least painful way to do it, and I came up with what I thought was the perfect plan. I was mentally and physically exhausted. I knew where my parents kept their medicine, and I figured the easiest way out would be to take a bunch of my mom's pills, go to sleep, and never wake up again. Compared to the life I was living, dying seemed easy."

The impact of her last statement took my breath away, and my nose began to tingle, preparing for a cry. "A natural response," I assured her. I was glad she never went through with it, of course, but I wanted her to know there was nothing wrong with suicide crossing her mind, given her horrific life circumstance. Still, life has a beautiful way of redeeming itself from the bleakest of times, if only you allow it too.

She laughed. "What saved me was that I always thought, *I don't want to live in hell for eternity, there is no way! I live in hell on earth, I should at least have..."*
"A good afterlife!" I said in unison with her, before we both broke out in laughter.
"It will be a nice life in heaven," she said looking at me warmly with a smile on her face.
She let me in on a secret weapon she used to ground herself. When thoughts of suicide rushed her, and she felt the sinister grips of her father's rotting roots tighten around her, pulling her into the darkness, she repeated a scripture to herself, over and over:
For I reckon that the sufferings of this present time are not worthy to be compared with the glory which shall be revealed in us. - Romans 8:18

Still, Esperanza was not safe from physical harm. Time after time she was taken down by the pound of her father's fists and his voyeuristic perversions.
It was New Year's Eve, 1978, and Esperanza was freshly 17. She, her brothers, and a big group of cousins and friends were hanging out in her brothers' room. Fernando, the first born, and Samuel, the third born, turned the garage into their bedroom, and given the big space, it was the go-to hangout zone for the younger generation. Meanwhile, all the parents hung out in the backyard drinking beers and tequila, dancing, eating tuna tostadas, carne asada, enchiladas — to name a few — and blasting Pepe Aguilar. It had all the makings of a lively and joyful gathering, but Hector quietly obsessed over what his daughter was doing inside.
While the cousins and friends waited for midnight to strike, one of Esperanza's cousins decided to make a food run, and he went around asking what everyone wanted. The next morning, Hector accused Esperanza of kissing her cousin. The best guess is Hector passed by the room when this cousin knelt down to reach Esperanza on the floor to get her order. There were between 15 and 20 teens in the room, including all

her brothers. Esperanza and her cousin were in no way alone, nor were they kissing or doing anything of the sort. Still, Hector insisted she was lying. Despite her impassioned defense, he beat her for it, badly.

The abuse didn't stop. Several months later, Esperanza was driving her parents around, because when Hector and Carmen went out, Esperanza was always forced to be their chauffeur — and as she was backing out of the liquor store parking lot her father whacked the car, making her think she hit something. He was drunk and trying to be funny, but she got scared.

"Why did you do that?!" she asked very seriously. "It's not funny."

He became agitated and told her to get out of the car and walk home. So, she did. Once she arrived, he beat her again, repeatedly screaming, "Why did you get out of the car?!" There was no sense to his actions.

When he beat her, he usually grabbed her head and hit it against the wall. This assured that bruises never showed on her body, and people never knew the truth.

As my mom recounts these stories to me from the dining room table, I am at once enraged and inspired. I let quiet take over as I tried and failed to form words, managing only sympathetic grunts. She smiled warmly at me.

"He hit my head a lot. That must be why I'm a little dingy," and just like that, we were laughing again.

"It seems he traded the sexual abuse for beatings as you got older," I deduced.

"There were also beatings when I was younger, because I would try and fight him off, which made him hit me even more." She paused. "But yes. The major, ugly beatings started as I got older. He was time and again seeing things that did not exist and using these made-up stories as an excuse to beat me. My mom rarely got in the middle." The pitch in her voice went up an octave, "You would think, as a mother, if your daughter is being beaten, you would do something to protect her!"

We both fell silent.

In the fall of 1979, Esperanza moved through her senior year of high school focused on one thing — becoming a nun. She always wanted to do missionary work and felt like being a nun, serving God and helping others, was her best opportunity. She also wasn't particularly interested in being sexually active given her traumatic upbringing with her father. She started to gather information and went to a convent in southern California to express her interest in joining.

Approaching the nuns at the convent was the first step in a long process. She went back home to let her parents know she wanted to become a nun. They were shocked and tried adamantly to talk her out of it.

"No! We will *not* allow you to become a nun! They will make you change your name and send you somewhere far away. We will never see you again!" they worried.

Esperanza raised her eyebrows at the idea of being sent far away and not seeing her parents. It was exactly what she wanted. But her parents insisted she not become a nun, and she still felt beholden to them, so she did not.

With every story my parents shared, my love and appreciation for them grew. The deeper we dug into this side of our family history, the more powerful I felt. What a spellbinding feeling to come together with your parents as they recall the experiences in life that had the greatest impacts on them, and so too on you. I relished in the gratitude I felt towards them for sharing their past pains and joys with me.

Engrossed in their past, I felt an evolution happening within my own being. I felt it stemming from my inner light, branching off to new heights. As a young child and adolescent, I was obsessed with the question: 'Who am I?' I see it written across all my journals, always questioning who I was, or rather, who I wanted to become. As I sit here today, I know that I simply always was. The core being of my soul has never changed. The pulsing heart within my body beats as it did when I was a little girl and before I could even speak, born from the heart that beats inside my own mother and father. I was me even before I was conceived.

10

It was the summer of 1980 and not long after announcing she wanted to be a nun — and having that dream halted by her parents — Esperanza and her brothers flew to Purepero, Mexico to visit their family. Ricardo and his family happened to be from the same small town and visiting at the same time for Ricardo's sister's wedding. He took the opportunity to ask Esperanza to the wedding. She accepted.

All dolled up and decked out, they bashfully watched as Ricardo's sister and brother-in law professed their love to one another at the traditional matrimonial mass, followed by a night of dancing in one another's arms. Esperanza let her guard down and gave into her feelings for Ricardo. This was the first time she started to feel love for him — gathered around with his parents and all eight brothers and sisters. She was enchanted.

The day after the wedding, Esperanza, Ricardo, and a couple of friends and siblings went on an adventure several hours away to hike around the volcano, Parícutin. That evening, once the group returned to Purepero, Ricardo and Esperanza walked around the plaza alone. The weather was humid and the slowly setting sun painted strokes across the sky of radiant blues, yellows, and oranges. They relaxed on a bench, sharing an ice cream from 'La Michoacána', Mexico's most iconic ice cream shop, as Ricardo worked up the courage to ask an imperative question.

"Esperanza, will you be my girlfriend?"

With Matt long in the rear view, she bashfully looked at Ricardo and felt her heart flutter. While he nervously awaited her answer, a big smile lit up her face. "Yes, I will."

Thus, began their lifelong adventure together. They were excited about building their future, unsure of all it would entail. But on this first night of Ricardo and Esperanza's union, they smiled in shared delight and basked in the initial feeling of love that still binds them together today.

In my parents backyard, more stories unfolded. With our feet on the firepit, I clung to the comfort of my dad's voice, as we slowly rocked back and forth in our rocking chairs.

"I knew your mom's family for years before I asked her to be my girlfriend. I met the Madero's through my cousin Victor who was close to them. He used to go to the park and have carne asada with your mom's family, and I would go with him. Your abuelito Hector was always highly attentive and helpful. I never thought anything more than: *Man, what a great family.*"

His voice quieted, as he stared out into the garden with a thoughtful expression, trying to make sense of the alternate reality he remembered. "I started getting to know them better, but still saw nothing out of the ordinary. It took a while to start realizing how strange things really were."

He began recalling the red flags. "Your mom and I were dating for a couple months, and we were hanging out in her parents' living room when, all of a sudden, her father came out of the bathroom *nude!* He walked out of the bathroom, down the hall, and into his bedroom *nude!*" The pitch in his voice became high with bewilderment.

"I saw him through these huge mirrors on the living room wall, opposite the bar, and it took me by surprise. I was speechless. I looked at your mom, and she looked at me, neither one of us saying a word. We eventually discussed it, but not until much later — which is when I found out this was a normal occurrence. At the time, I was either afraid of hearing the truth or afraid I was misinterpreting what was going on.

"When I think about it now, there are many things that did not make sense. When we hung out at her parents' house, he was never anywhere I could see him, yet he somehow saw everything. I know now he was spying on me through his bedroom window that looked into the family room. He was wondering if I was going to try and kiss your mom.

"This one time, the day before Halloween actually, your mom and I were seated on the couch in the family room. I was looking at her, giving her compliments, and I gave her a kiss on the cheek. Almost immediately, your abuelito Hector appeared out of nowhere! He grabbed me by the collar of my shirt and started forcing me out the door, into the street. I tried to speak but he started yelling over me, telling me I was disrespectful and to never come back. I was shocked and thought there was definitely something mentally wrong with this man."

"You did think that?!" I asked eagerly, relieved people were recognizing the signs of a monster.

"Oh yes, I did. I was only giving your mom a kiss on the cheek!" he stated with absurdity.

This marked a turning point for my parents, with suspicion and panic awakening my dad to a darker reality, and a new sense of security giving my mom greater hope. My mom later told to me that the day after my dad was kicked out for giving her a kiss on the cheek, her father erupted in a manner more violent than usual.

It was the night of Halloween 1981, and the streets were crowded with eager trick-or-treaters. Daniel and Leo, 14 and 15 years old, were among them. Fernando no longer lived at home and Samuel was out with friends. Esperanza was in her bedroom when, all of a sudden, her father barged in yelling.
"I saw you making out with your boyfriend yesterday!"
"What are you talking about? He just gave me a kiss on the cheek!" she shot back.
Shouting at each other, they argued over the truth she knew and the one he was embellishing. Esperanza tensed up, fearful of what was coming next. Her father's evil demeanor grew a new darkness. The truth did not matter. Hector needed a reason to rage at her, and he had one — even if it was false.
He cornered his daughter and raised his clenched fist, striking her arms furiously, clutching her hair and pounding her head against the wall. Carmen, upon hearing the chaos, ran to Esperanza's room, yelling and pleading with Hector to leave her alone. In an instant of fury, he turned to his wife and grabbed her tightly by the throat, shoving her backwards before turning back around to batter his daughter some more.
Many of the neighboring trick-or-treaters and their parents heard Esperanza and Carmen's outcries and Hector's destructive madness, and ran to find Daniel and Leo. Esperanza's two brothers appeared in record time, and the neighbors rushed in after them, looking to protect in any way they could. Indeed, the scene inside the Madero home was sheer turmoil. Daniel, greatly disturbed, began to bawl and plead with his father to stop. Leo, enraged, charged his father, pushed him up against the wall, and punched him in the face.
Hector stumbled forward, trying to catch his balance in shock. Neighbors gathered around Esperanza, comforting her with hugs and

gentle words while Leo pushed his father out of his sister's room. It was a haunting sight, resembling Elena's marked fate at 14 with her now deceased husband, dragging her down the dirt road, and frightening the neighborhood.

The rest of the night was tense and uncomfortable. Esperanza's brothers kept by her side, not allowing their father anywhere near her. Leo questioned his father's behavior, but still did not see the totality of his malevolence. No one did. For Esperanza's brothers, this ruthless event was quite unexpected. But from then on, Esperanza felt more protected. Situations like these solidified her faith in at least one familial tie, the one she had with her brothers.

Growing up, when Daniel and Leo were still too small, she felt secure with Fernando and Samuel, but more so with Samuel. With only a 12-month age gap, he played the role of older brother honorably, regardless of being the younger one. After that Halloween, she knew she could count on Leo and Daniel, too. Out of all her brothers, Leo was the most level-headed, but if you messed with him, you were in trouble. That night, his father messed with his sister, and that meant he messed with Leo.

When Samuel returned home a little later, Carmen piled everyone in the car to go to Fernando's house. She was fed up with Hector and finally took action against her family's abusive figurehead. She wanted to be away from Hector's manipulation and savageness, for not only her children but for herself. While at Fernando's, all heated in their own right, the family got a call. One of their cousins was in a fatal accident in Tijuana.

The news instantly changed everything. Hector came and picked Carmen and Esperanza up, and the three drove down to Tijuana as a trio, leaving the boys behind. There was a double standard in their home — like in many homes — where the boys are allowed to do what they want, while the girl, Esperanza, had no choice but to follow her parents' orders. She went where her parents went. They came back from Mexico and the violent Halloween rampage was long forgotten.

Hearing this story gave me a glimpse of the strength I so wished Abuelita Carmen to possess, only to have it vanish quickly. These flashes of hope for my mom were all too fleeting.

"My brothers and I never talked about that night," she pressed on. "Matters like that were not discussed or communicated when we were growing up. And my brothers did not know the extent of the situation because my father would touch me when they were not around. To them, that beating happened out of the blue.

"It took me a while to tell your dad about that night, but from then on, we were never allowed to be alone in the family room. We could only sit in the main room, or in the kitchen with everybody else."

🕊

As Esperanza and Ricardo's courtship progressed, he gradually noticed more odd behavior from her parents. In May of 1982, Esperanza and Ricardo were 20 and 25 years old. He invited Esperanza on a date to see the newly released film E.T. The potential to be alone with her, outside of her home, holding her hand in the theater, excited him greatly. And to both of their surprise, Esperanza's parents said they would allow it.

To their greater surprise, when Ricardo arrived at the Madero home to pick up Esperanza, Carmen and Hector got in the car with them. Ricardo was in a state of shock, realizing it would be the four of them on the date. It quickly became an uncomfortable evening. Ricardo was made to pay for the four of them, and Carmen and Hector settled in the seats directly behind them. Ricardo felt Hector's glare upon him, watching his every move instead of watching the movie. Ricardo and Esperanza, not even able to hold hands, were seated next to one another like strangers. The movie ended, the date concluded, romance was denied.

Several weeks later, Ricardo decided to invite Esperanza to a fancy dinner. The restaurant was called Tigers and was well-known for its premium steaks and decadent sides. The restaurant was advertising a special of 16 dollars per plate, and back then, that was a lot of money for Ricardo. He asked Esperanza if she would like to go to dinner, and her parents told her she could. The day came for Ricardo to pick Esperanza up for their romantic dinner and, sure enough, Carmen and Hector walked out of the house, and climbed into the car with them.

Ricardo laughed quietly to himself at the absurdity of the situation. He was certain he could afford two plates, but four? He was freaking out. To top it off, Hector ordered a shot and Ricardo thought, *Oh great, there goes another three bucks!* He was dreading not having enough money to pay for the dinner, but luckily, he did. It just meant cutting down on spending and eating for the next week to make up for it.

🕊

Looking back, all my dad could do was laugh.

"Let's just say I was on a tight budget for a little bit after that," he said laughing. His tone quickly turned bitter. "That was the end. I never invited your mom out again while we were dating. I never felt comfortable. We were supposedly 'dating' for a few years, but what we did was not dating at all. We never had any time by ourselves and were made to watch a lot of novelas — Mexican soap operas — with Abuelita Carmen.

"Your abuelito acted far from normal when it came to his adult daughter and her boyfriend. He was never normal when it came to your mom. The only reason I noticed anything was because we were dating. It is unfortunately part of the ugly life your mom lived, and it didn't take long to realize they were not a healthy family."

Shortly after the E.T. incident, and towards the end of Esperanza's junior year at University of California Irvine, her grades began to slip. Keeping her grades up was always a point of pride for Esperanza, and after receiving scholarships to pay for her tuition, books, and boarding — though her parents surely never let her board — she was under additional pressure. Her scholarship could not withstand the drop in grades. Esperanza had always thrown herself into school to distract from her problems at home, and attributed the slip to not having a quiet, peaceful place to study.

Her parents did not care much about her studies, while still expecting only the best out of her. They never left her home alone, and instead continued to make her go everywhere they went. When she was home doing schoolwork, her parents would often interrupt to have her help with chores. The chaos of three younger brothers running around, blasting music, and living their unrestricted lives did not help either. She decided to return to the same convent she went to years earlier to see if they would allow her to live there for her senior year of college.

She decided against telling her mom and dad until she knew it was possible. They never allowed her to live away from home and shot down the idea of her living on campus when she was accepted to UCI, so she took measured precautions before broaching the subject. To Esperanza's delight, the convent confirmed a space for her starting in August. Esperanza was ecstatic. She went back to her parents to let them know she would be moving into the convent for her last year of school. She made her decision and was not letting her parents interfere. Carmen and Hector were disturbed by her return to this idea and tried swaying her in another direction. They offered to get her an apartment instead, but Esperanza did not want anything from them, and her mind was made up.

She gave them an ultimatum: "Let me live at the convent while I finish school, or I will quit school altogether to become a nun." Either way, she was moving to the convent. She no longer wanted to be a nun — she was in love with Ricardo — but simply yearned for a comfortable place to live, where she could focus on her studies and find some calm. Feeling backed into a corner, her parents let her go.

On one of her visits back home from the convent, Esperanza was taking a shower, and to her surprise she turned around and there was her father, peeping in at her through a small window, just staring. She screamed and slammed the window shut. He played it off the same way he played off all his deviant behaviors — as if it never happened at all. She decided to visit home less and less.

Esperanza's strength grew with every decision she took into her own hands. At her new home, she was excited to be surrounded by women and girls she respected, have her own room where she could lock the door — plus, her best friend from college, Miriam, decided to join her. Esperanza felt empowered. A pressure released from her body. Being out of her parents' home was liberating. With all the peace, quiet, and girl talk she could ask for, she was in her own little heaven. She and Miriam would dip in the jacuzzi night after night, conversing about life and giggling, before retiring to their adjacent rooms. She was exactly where she deserved to be.

11

From the sanctuary of the garden, I asked my dad to describe how he proposed to my mom. He immediately burst into laughter.

"Oh brother," he said, shaking his head. "The proposal should be the subject of a comic book. I was not thinking straight. I proposed over the phone, and not even directly! I never asked if she would like to be my wife, instead I asked what she would say if I asked her to be my wife. She told me to ask her directly, and I again got nervous and said: 'Okay, hmmm, but what would you say, yes or no?'"

Throwing our heads back, we laughed in harmony.

"She eventually said yes on the call, but her father would not have it. He would not allow her to get married, let alone engaged. According to him your mom was too young, but in hindsight, I'm sure there were other reasons. He declined our engagement for a year. After that, I sent my cousin Victor to speak to him on my behalf.

"Remember, our culture used to approach proposals by sending a close relative or priest to ask on one's behalf. Victor went to speak to your abuelitos, and afterwards came back to let me know I had the greenlight. Your abuelito finally said yes. Anyways, that was the proposal. Over the phone. Not even: 'Would you like to be my wife', but 'what would you say if...'"

We erupted in more laughter and he rolled his eyes at his younger self.

My mom remembered her father's disapproval.

"My father never said yes. After a year of him saying no, I told him, 'Ricardo is going to send someone to come ask for my hand in marriage again, and this time it does not matter what you say. It's happening whether you agree to it or not,' and I walked out of the room."

Esperanza decided to write Ricardo a letter revealing more about the reality of her family life before they said their "I dos." She wrote and rewrote *Dear Ricardo*, until she had a short, to the point, and loving letter she felt comfortable with him reading.

Alone for once in her parents' backyard, she mustered up the courage to pull the letter out and hand it to him.

"What is this?" Ricardo asked, grinning.

"Just read it. Once you're done with it, we're going to burn it," she said with a nervous smirk.

Ricardo smiled back at her, got comfortable on the brick ledge of the planters, and opened the letter. Esperanza's heart raced with fear and Ricardo's smile quickly faded as he read about his love's traumatic past. Esperanza wanted him to know the truth about her father and what he did to her. She wanted to relieve herself of this crushing secret before they got married, and to be able to express herself about it with her soon-to-be husband freely. He needed to know. Ricardo was in complete shock and felt as if it were all a dream. He felt removed, like he was floating away from his body.

Ricardo watched Esperanza pace back and forth from the corner of his eye before she walked back towards him once again. They stared at each other in deafening silence. Esperanza bravely, but nervously asked, "What do you think? I understand if you no longer want to get married."

"I am in love with you. It doesn't matter. I don't care. I want to marry you. We are going to have a different life. A beautiful life together. This changes nothing about my love for you and my desire to build a future with you." He paused shortly before continuing. "The only thing I need to know is that we are getting married."

Esperanza smiled, feeling her love come from deep within her gut. "Okay. I just wanted you to know," she reiterated anxiously.

Facing one another on the brick ledge, Ricardo responded, "You have done your part by sharing this with me. I still want to marry you."

Volleying his gaze between Esperanza and his feet, he held her hands tightly, silently trying to process what he just learned: *Maybe he's not really her dad. There is no way a real father could do that to his daughter, is there? What a monster! She is so brave.*

With little time to reconcile this rough revelation together, their hearts were heavy. The newly engaged couple looked at each other and shared a perfunctory smile. Ricardo felt the need to vomit, his insides mixing uncontrollably. Esperanza's parents were inside the house mere feet away, with no idea about the truths uncovered outside.

Adamant about burning the letter, Esperanza pulled matches out of her pocket, holding them up with a single nod. They stood, and with Ricardo holding the letter steadily, she lit a match and brought the flame close, lighting the letter on fire. The paper burned quickly, orange and blue flames expanding, black and grey smoke ascending slowly into the sky. Ricardo and Esperanza stood side by side, muted, watching the flames engulf the truth, every word of freedom ashing back into the earth.

Sitting around the firepit, I looked at my dad's soft gaze and relaxed posture, smiling at the person he was and all that he gave me in life. He drank his water, staring out in front of him, thinking of the days, weeks, and months after he first found out that the love of his life was molested by her own father since she was a little girl.

"I was sad. I did not want to look at him. I could not stop thinking of how horrible of a person he was," my dad recalled. "Your mom was noticeably afraid of him, to the point where even when we were alone, which were very few times, she was afraid. We were going to pre-marital classes, and on the way back I would try and hug her, and she would not let me. 'What if my father is following us, what if, what if…' She was afraid of every little interaction. It was sad. That 'what if' was always in the back of her mind. I did not want to question anything because within a few months we were going to be husband and wife, and then it would be completely different."

He spoke calmly, slowly, and thoughtfully. "I wish I would have had the strength to say: 'We are going to get rid of them. We are never going to allow them to be in our lives again.' But I didn't."

I mustered up a sorrowful "hmmmm" and we let the quietness wash over us for a little longer, basking in life's 'what if's'.

12

Once again, we found ourselves surrounded by old pictures and photo albums. As my mom and I rifled through memories on the living room floor, I hit the record button on my recorder, and she began.

"This is the wedding album of Esperanza Madero to Ricardo Rodriguez," she remembered with a smile on her face and a glow in her eyes. She laughed seeing a picture of my dad. "I cannot get over how young your dad looks. I must have talked him out of the hat..." she remembered fondly. I could only imagine.

My dad looked dapper, and I could not help but admire him in his all-white tail suit, complete with a cane. My mom's wedding dress was stunning, made of lace with small beaded flowers lining her body in a collared V-neck, stretching down the arms to create two beautiful fitted lace sleeves, coming to a delicate point on the back of her hands. Her veil was long and draped a second layer of thin lace along the train of her dress. The groomsmen wore all black tuxedos with pink flowers pinned on their left breast, while the bridesmaids donned pale pink floor-length dresses, holding pink laced fans with fascinators on their heads.

I loved looking back at the culmination of my parents' love in these snapshots, the styles and rhythms of a different time. It's always interesting to look at your parents' lives before you were born, realizing they themselves had their own adventures and dreams before you came along. I watched my mom being taken back to a feeling of real happiness during a time when those were rare.

I turned to her and asked, "Did Abuelita or Abuelito have a conversation about marriage with you before your wedding?"

"No. They may have had a conversation with your dad though," she alluded.

Indeed, Hector sat Ricardo down to have the "marriage talk" before the wedding. Ricardo stared at his soon-to-be father-in-law in the otherwise empty Madero living room. As he nodded his head in silent participation, the sounds and sights around him blurred. Knowing what he knew about the man before him, nothing Hector said was resonating. Ricardo felt woozy as he focused on Hector's face.

The complete mistrust in Hector's words made Ricardo hear them as near nonsense, spoken in a low murmur, as he stared blankly at Hector. His vacancy was taken as wedding nerves. The exchange meant nothing to Ricardo, knowing the true character of the man before him. The two men finished the conversation and Ricardo walked out the door, letting all of Hector's meaningless advice drift from his mind forever.

The process of planning the wedding was a nightmare for Esperanza, even though Ricardo did most of it, including paying for the entire thing. Beholden to the unpredictable moods of her parents, Esperanza felt the weight of those rotting roots tighten, holding her back from the life she wanted, the life she deserved. She was not allowed to go anywhere with Ricardo and talking to her mother about the wedding was sure to cause an argument or leave her sobbing — yet another opportunity blown by Carmen to be there for her daughter. Strangely, yet fortunately, Hector stayed out of the wedding plans, avoiding all related conversation when he could, mourning the impending loss of his identity that was so attached to his daughter. How would he release his rage now that she was leaving his home for good? He would find a way.

In August of 1983, Ricardo stood at the altar, staring at Esperanza in awe as she walked down the aisle, a stunning sight of grace and poise. It was a beautiful moment in Ricardo and Esperanza's lives, despite the bizarre chaos of how they got there — how she got there. Ricardo's attention shifted to Hector, walking Esperanza down the aisle. He felt his heart clench thinking of the hypocrisy this man encapsulated, the values he purported to uphold, but in truth betrayed with every chance. Today, however, Ricardo got to marry the love of his life and nothing would stand in his way. He let his focus return to his blushing bride.

Ricardo killed two pigs to serve carnitas and hired all the servers. Michelle, April, and other friends of Esperanza's went to the reception hall during the mass to decorate. It was a glorious day despite the malignant presence of the mother and father of the bride. Almost every time Esperanza turned to look at her mother, she was crying. One of the people Esperanza was supposed to enjoy this day most with, her mother, instead made it about herself, turning woeful. Undoubtedly, Carmen and Hector, were bracing themselves for the loss of the queen in their twisted, sadistic game of chess.

℘

Huddled with my mom on the living room carpet, I asked a question I knew the answer to.

"Were you ever harsh with your parents?"

"Never. I never ever disrespected either of them," she stated proudly. I cut her off, trying to make sure she understood what I was trying to ask. "Not disrespected, just…."

She interrupted, knowing exactly what I was getting at. "No. I never put my foot down. Not until after I got married," she said, this time with hints of sadness.

"Not like we did?" I asked, laughing at the numerous times my siblings and I challenged our parents.

"Never," she responded while chuckling and shaking her head.

"Why not?" I asked.

"I was terrified of them, and that terror kept me from lashing out. It was not out of strength or restraint, rather intense fear." Her memory of not having stood her ground was as vivid as could be. I could sense the irritation fuming off her skin. "After giving birth, I felt powerful, and that is when I became aggressive. It was not until after becoming a mother that I truly understood that what happened to me was not my fault. It was a long trek to get there, but I was no longer afraid of my parents."

We flipped to a picture of my parents kissing at a park on their wedding day and I immediately recalled a detail I had to dig into.

"Was this your first kiss together?" I asked with a mischievous grin.

"Yes," said my mom quite definitively. "We did not kiss at the mass or the reception. We did not kiss in front of people. Really, our first kiss was in the car after the ceremony. Your dad's best friend drove us around and took us from the church to the reception, where we took these pictures in the park. We had our first kiss in the backseat," she said beaming.

"You never kissed before?" I asked, still flabbergasted at this reality. My mom shook her head no. "Not once while you were dating?" I was in steadfast disbelief, even after hearing it my whole life.

"Nope." The innocence in her voice radiated all around me. My voice rose as I laughed in shock. "Not even when you were alone?!"

My mom was getting irritated by this point, chuckling and rolling her eyes at me, thinking little of their delayed affection. "No! The answer is not going to change. We were never really alone." My mom flipped through pictures, waiting for my state of shock to pass. I gave a final chuckle and left it at that.

I could not resist bringing this topic back up with my dad, so on another day, I dove back in.

"When was your first kiss with Mami?" I asked, just wanting to re-hear his version of the story.

"The day we got married!" he exclaimed with a big smile on his face. "It was after the mass."

"That is crazy!" I echoed my shock.

"It is crazy! Yes, indeed," he said with a smirk, allowing the memories to envelope him. In truth, as shocked as I was, I was moved by my parents devotion to one another, the purity of their love, and how far they came together.

During Esperanza and Ricardo's wedding, while Carmen was crying, Esperanza wondered what her father must be thinking. She looked at her new husband and smiled, thinking about what a happy, supportive mother-in-law she would be when their inevitable kids married. It was easy for her to imagine this far ahead and helped her in times of waning hope.

The newlyweds danced the night away to the live band, indulging with their siblings, friends, and family. Meanwhile, Hector was excessively drunk, putting Esperanza on edge. She knew it was only a matter of time before he became aggressive.

His particular brand of mental abuse was heavy on the manipulation. When it came time to leave the reception, it was no surprise he had a plan up his sleeve. He drunkenly demanded that Esperanza — in her wedding gown on her wedding night — drive him home. She relented, fearful of a bigger scene, and drove her parents home with Ricardo following closely behind. Hector needed to overpower his daughter one last time, before he lost complete control of her forever.

Ricardo rented an apartment a month before they got married, and after dropping Esperanza's parents off, the newlyweds went to begin their new life in their new home. The next day, they left on their honeymoon to

Yosemite with the money they got from the dollar dance — a Mexican wedding tradition where guests line up to wish the couple well, pinning money on them just before dancing together. For the first time in their relationship, the couple was alone together. Finally. They felt free. Driving the open roads, they felt sheer joy and lightness in their every move, ready to deepen their bond.

On one of their adventures, Ricardo and Esperanza stopped in an orchard of apple trees. Ricardo climbed up one of the trees and shouted down to Esperanza that he was going to shake some apples loose. Esperanza took her position under the tree ready to catch, but of course as Ricardo shook the branches, a rush of apples came falling on her head, and she ran out from under the tree. Exploding in laughter, she looked back at an already hysterical Ricardo. They had apples!

Beyond sheer joy, Esperanza felt safe with Ricardo, even when it came time to sexual intimacy. This was a man she loved, and a man she chose to be with. This was different. Their embrace was full of love and she reveled in its security. This did not mean she was free from intimacy challenges — far from it. She would many times have visceral flashbacks to her stolen innocence, making affection feel cringe worthy. But she was growing stronger against these reflexes, and mostly felt free from harm. She was in love.

After their honeymoon, the apartment they returned to — the one they would start calling home — had no refrigerator, no table to eat on, no TV. The dining room table was a small trash can flipped upside down with a plank of wood on top. They used an ice chest to keep their food cold. Every two or three days, Ricardo would stop by the store and get a bag of ice for what little they had. After paying for the wedding, and spending the dollar dance money on the honeymoon, Ricardo and Esperanza had only 25 dollars left in their checking account. Yet still, nothing could get in the way of their newfound happiness and Esperanza's first ever feeling of true freedom.

The newlyweds saved what they could, Esperanza working as a preschool director and teacher, and Ricardo as a welder. Soon they had enough to buy a mobile home in Fountain Valley, where they became part of a community. They saw potential in that little mobile home, however run-down from the previous owner's neglect. After moving in, Esperanza and Ricardo painted the entire house, fixed up what needed fixing, and worked hard on the garden. They were only there for a short time, but the husband and wife were finding their way, finding peace at last for Esperanza.

I was proud of all the hard work my parents put in and how far they had come. Imagining this time in my parents' lives was like watching an 80s rom com directed by Stanley Kubrick. I stared at a picture of my parents on their honeymoon, each with their signature look, my dad with his mustache and my mom with her short puffy hair. Their natural good looks were undeniable, their sense of style giving away the decade.

Knowing where my parents came from, and where they are now has always been a source of great inspiration for me. I am eternally grateful to my parents and paternal grandparents for working as hard as they have to provide their children with the best life and opportunities they could. I was instilled with the quality of humbleness and with the belief that with hard work I can achieve anything, including the life of my dreams.

It was 1984 and love was dancing all around, with Esperanza and Ricardo's love flourishing. Fernando and Gloria — Esperanza's oldest brother and Ricardo's younger sister — fell in love and married as well. Samuel — Esperanza's almost twin — started dating the girl who would eventually become his wife, Jessica.

As Jessica began to infiltrate the solid family unit, with Carmen and Hector still at the helm, it did not take long for her to wisen to their faults and flaws. She found herself in many uncomfortable situations with Hector, and quickly became irritated with Carmen's love for money and drama.

It started the first time Samuel took Jessica home. She was greeted with more affection than she wanted, as Hector pulled her in close, grabbed her face, and gave her a kiss on the mouth. Taken aback, she became stiff, quickly realizing Samuel had not seen. From that day forward, she was uncomfortable in Hector's presence. Though he greeted her in this exact way for an entire year, Hector and Carmen's position of influence kept her from speaking up. It was quickly apparent to her that Hector and Carmen were at the top of the totem pole. They were everything to everyone. After one year of improper greetings, she put a stop to the kissing by quickly turning her face. She would not let him take advantage of her anymore.

In the early part of 2018, Tía Jessica spoke her truth for the first time. Surrounded by crystals and incense, Tía Jessica and I settled on her bed, the smell of palo santo filling our every breath. She had never before shared with anyone — not even Tío Samuel — the disturbing kisses from her now father-in-law. I listened, her voice low and secretive, with a hint of eagerness and relief in finally voicing what she had buried for decades. I smiled, honored she felt safe enough to share with me.

"Your grandparents always had money, and still, they made all their kids give them their money. Samuel worked hard and gave his mom most of his check every month. She would walk into his room on payday with one hand out, palm up, slapping it over and over again with the other hand, asking him for the money. He would hug her, hand her his money, kiss her on the cheek, and she would laugh. Another one of her money hungry habits was rubbing her thumb, index, and middle finger together and saying, 'Cash money, Cash money.'"

My mind flashed to a comment my mom once made while relaxing on the living room rug. She shook her head as thoughts of her mother came to the fore. "Instead of being a giving person, my mom was more of a 'gimme gimme gimme' person. My father giving her money was one thing, but making her kids give her their money was another. I owed my parents nothing, and yet until I got married, I was required to give my mom the little money I earned."

I quickly grinned thinking how lucky I was to not have a mother like that before tía Jessica's voice brought me back to the present moment: "Your grandmother is one of the most dramatic people I know. She has this loud cry she would let out when she did not feel well."

Tía Jessica let out a wail imitating Abuelita Carmen's infamous sound, like that of a woman pretending to faint, "Oooooooh."

"The first time I heard that wail," she went on "I was sixteen and we were hanging out in the backyard. All of the women and your grandma's sons ran to her. People started asking what was wrong, and instead of answering the question she carried on with her dramatic cries. I just thought, *What the hell is this?*

"Your grandpa came in like a shining knight, in a deep collected voice, with one eyebrow raised, sounding like Gaston from Beauty and the Beast: 'My wife's blood pressure is out of control! My wife, my wife, my wife.' She was feeling ill, but it was easy to see she was being overly dramatic, a common theme with her. She would walk around in the sparkliest, most expensive outfits, like a peacock, always strutting.

"Regardless of your grandparents, I learned a lot about love from the rest of the family — the value of hugging and kissing on the cheek when you greet someone, the importance of community within a family, and the admiration that is formed around respecting your elders. I felt like it was a super close-knit, healthy, happy family. Your grandma was an amazing cook, had these boys who thought she walked on water, a beautiful daughter, and a husband who gave her anything she wanted. She had it all — or so we thought."

Around this same time, Esperanza and Ricardo were living in their new mobile home when they got pregnant with their first child. They were ecstatic and, in the spring of 1985, Valentina Esperanza Rodriguez was born. Esperanza's and Ricardo's families gathered around in the hospital room, celebrating the first-born girl on the Madero side.

When it came time for the inaugural breastfeeding, Esperanza looked at her father and kindly asked him to leave the room. She watched as his face morphed into anger but stood her ground and stared right back at him. Breastfeeding a baby is one of the most natural and beautiful human acts, but she knew her father's sick mind all too well. He would find a way to pervert it.

Hector fumed as he stared his daughter down, allowing her a few seconds longer to change her mind. She did not.

The OB-GYN — who happened to be male — walked in, helping ease the tension. Esperanza looked down at Valentina in her arms and casually pressed her father one last time, "Please, Dad."

Carmen covered up the awkwardness with smiles, patting her husband on the arm, warmly saying they would wait outside. Hector fixated on his daughter with smoldering eyes. Desperately playing the role of the honorable, caring father for the doctor, he left the room. Later, he made sure to let his daughter know how angry he was that a "random" male was allowed to remain in the room for breastfeeding while he was not. Esperanza and Ricardo were too mesmerized with their newborn daughter to let Hector bother them. They shook it off with a growing ease.

Just two months later, Ricardo and Esperanza were basking in the joy of first-time parenthood when they received an evacuation letter.

"This letter says we gotta move!" exclaimed Ricardo, reading it in disbelief.

"What do you mean we have to move?" Esperanza asked, confused.

"Apparently this is not a family community!"

Esperanza stood up and took the letter from his hands to read it herself. Ricardo joked that had he known, he would have hidden Valentina for a few more months. The two laughed as they planned their next steps.

In their search for affordable houses, Ricardo and Esperanza came across a beautiful two-story home with a big front and back yard. Although the couple knew it was out of their reach, Esperanza said with brimming hope, "They don't charge to look, right?"

The new parents fell in love with every corner of the place. They returned home with an odd feeling of luck.

"Let's make an offer on the house," Ricardo proposed, wide-eyed.

"Yeah, but how?" Esperanza asked, perplexed.

"Why don't we just go over there and offer what we can afford. I know it's less than the asking price, but let's see what the owners say."

They drove back to their dream home and a nervous Esperanza told Ricardo she would wait for him in the car. It was about time to breastfeed anyways. Ricardo walked back into the open house to negotiate with the homeowner, Laurie.

"We really like the house. We would love to raise our kids in it," Ricardo stated.

"How many kids do you have?" Laurie asked.

"One right now, but we are planning on having more."

"That's great. How come your wife didn't come with you?"

"She did! But she didn't want to come in because she thought we were going to offer too little."

"How much do you have in mind?"

Ricardo proceeded with their offer and all their reasons for falling in love with the home. Laurie looked at Ricardo with a smile and said, "Tell your wife to come in."

Ricardo ran out to the car, "Esperanza! Laurie wants you to come in!"

"Are you sure?" Esperanza asked nervously.

"Yeah! Come on!"

Esperanza got out of the car with Valentina and the three of them walked back into the house together.

"Oooooh, what is the baby's name?" Laurie asked excitedly.

"Valentina," said Esperanza lovingly.

"Oh! That's my best friend's name!" Laurie said with a twinkle in her eye.

An immediate connection formed. Laurie looked at the three of them adoringly. "You know, I raised my kids in this house. It is an excellent neighborhood."

"What do you think about the offer?" Ricardo asked plainly.

"I like the offer," Laurie said to their great surprise. "My husband will be home soon and we can finalize everything."

Ricardo and Esperanza could not believe what they were hearing. It seemed life was on their side, the pieces were falling into place, and they would soon have their own corner of the world to put down new roots for their growing family. They walked around the house, fantasizing about the life they would build in the home, and the memories they would form. Laurie's husband arrived, and the four of them ironed out the details. Ricardo and Esperanza were consumed with elation, feeling the natural high of starting their dream life together.

They scrambled for the first couple of years to make their payments, but that did not deter them from having another child. In the fall of 1986, Amelia Christy Rodriguez was born — Hi, that's me. Esperanza and Ricardo were in absolute love — in love with each other, in love with their growing family, in love with their home, and in love with life.

Esperanza held frequent yard sales to help make payments, while Ricardo held his full-time job as supervisor of a welding and sales team. The couple's hard work was paying off. Enjoying their new bounty of blessings, Esperanza and Ricardo tried mightily to bury the secret about her father. But like all problems that go unaddressed, Hector — his tyranny of sexual abuse, and the trauma that dragged heavily behind it — rattled like a ticking time bomb, shaking toward its inevitable explosion.

I could hear the grief and guilt in my dad's voice when he said, "The worst part is, your abuelito Hector was in our lives for many years. I do not know why we allowed that. I should have told him, 'Now that we are married, and have kids, I never want to see you again.' But how can you say that to your wife's father or to your wife? 'Hey, let's tell your mother and father we never want to see them again.' Still, it blows my mind that we allowed him near our children. People like your abuelito do not change easily."

Riding the waves of each story, each conversation imparting deeper insight, I wanted to know what the communication around the sexual abuse my mother endured as a child was like in the beginning of my parents' marriage. I asked them separately how this topic was handled, starting with my mom.

"Your dad never asked me questions. He closed it off, and I understand that," she explained. "He could not deal with it. As the years went on, he started to allow himself to listen. We can talk about it a lot more openly now."

My dad answered with sincerity and strength. "We tried. We did, but it was challenging. At times she wanted to talk but, unfortunately for her, I was not prepared for anything like this. I did not give her the attention she needed. Not wanted — needed. We talked about it a few times, but it was excruciating beyond belief, so I subconsciously decided it was not healthy to discuss. I was wrong! Talking it out would have been much better for our relationship's health, and for hers more than anybody else's.

"When you first start to speak about trauma, you relive it. Not physically of course, but mentally, and that affects you physically, but that is how you start to heal your struggles. Now we can discuss it without a problem. Your mom went through hell with your grandpa, but I still wanted a life with her. Why would I not? Being molested was not a choice she made. It was her father's. She had nothing to hide from me. She never did. We cannot change the past, but we can ask ourselves: *What can I do to help my partner now and into the future?*"

This makes me think of the caregivers, standing by their partner's side in the wake of intense trauma. We often overlook their struggles, focused rightfully on the survivor. But we must not forget the emotional weight our partners carry for us and the strength that requires. We must remember this the next time a partner finds these topics hard to discuss. It's not a reason not to have them, but a call to action to allow the love to flow both ways.

It was December 25th of 1987 and the families gathered around the Christmas tree at the Madero home. The sight was of a growing family, with Valentina and Amelia now two and one years old, Fernando and Gloria with their two small children, and Samuel and Jessica recently engaged. An excited Jessica opened her gift from Samuel. It was a beautiful set of diamond and pearl earrings. In her excitement, she showed everyone else her gift, putting the earrings on and feeling grateful to soon be officially part of the Madero tribe.

Out of nowhere comes Carmen, parading in front of the family, grabbing her ears and pointing to the same exact earrings, only bigger.

"Look! Look! Samuel gave them to me." Her childish theatrics did not impress anyone. Later, it was revealed that when Carmen heard Samuel bought Jessica those earrings, she became upset and guilted Samuel into buying her an even larger pair of the same exact design.

Shortly after Christmas, Samuel told his mother he was saving his money to buy a home for himself and Jessica, and therefore would not be able to give her any more money. This, of course, upset Carmen, and she made it known, asking Samuel where her money was for several months after. It would take her a while to accept that she would no longer receive money from her son, or rather that her son now had another woman in his life.

Valentina and Amelia were now four and two years old, and in the spring of 1989, the sisters were beyond excited to welcome their baby brother, Ricardo Rodriguez Jr., to the family and to their now triangle of siblings, calling him Ricky from there on out. Esperanza and Ricardo were floating in love all over again with their new baby boy.

There was much to celebrate, and as most Mexican families do, Esperanza and Ricardo's families gathered often. The fourth generation was born into a tight-knit community of families, with Hector and Carmen still at the top of the totem pole. All the siblings, friends, tías, tíos, and kids, along with Hector and Carmen, spent most weekends together, with feats and laughter, the burden of Hector's true evil a heavier and heavier secret to keep.

In the summer of 1989, on family trips out to the desert, Hector would be up early in his tighty whities, bathing in the outside shower. He would then step out, go up to the campfire where all the kids were playing, and reignite the flames as if his tighty whities weren't completely see-through.

Despite Hector's perverted eccentricities, most remember those trips fondly. Afterall, Esperanza and her brothers were a close group of siblings, and their children were best friends. There was a lot of love and light, kids running around playing in the desert, newborn babies to coddle, mini pools to cool off in, and adults having the time of their lives on dune buggies. From a bird's eye view, life was fantastic. Yet a closer look revealed a molding air all around Hector, floating in the unseen vibrations all around him, spreading to his family and friends.

Unfortunately, Hector and Carmen were not the only source of devastating trauma during this time.

13

At the end of summer of 1989, Esperanza and Ricardo went up against a new family battle; one no less agonizing than the darkness of Esperanza's childhood. Experienced in fight, the young parents were suddenly facing a war closer to their hearts than any they had fought before, with more to lose and more to win. This would come to be one of the most trying events of their lives — and the catalyst to finally propel Esperanza into therapy for the first time in her life.

Therapy is a crucial step in recovering from trauma, and one Esperanza quickly learned would have been immensely helpful years earlier. But she had not yet understood the weight of her own silence. It would take a different kind of love, the unconditional maternal love she had cultivated within, and an unspeakable test of that love, to make her realize the value of her mental stability. Although still horrified at the events that pushed her to therapy, Esperanza was grateful they led her to where she needed to be.

It was a Friday night. Ricardo's dad, Antonio — who was working in California at the time — took his children and their spouses out to dinner. Esperanza and Ricardo enjoyed a night free of children, with Valentina, Amelia, and Ricky, just four months old, at home with the nanny, Barbara. When the adults returned from dinner, Valentina and Amelia were downstairs playing. Esperanza and Ricardo greeted the girls and played with them for a few minutes before saying goodnight to Barbara and heading upstairs with their daughters. Midway up, they could hear Ricky crying and screaming.

Their parental instincts lurched them both into action. Esperanza tried to breastfeed, thinking he was hungry, but that didn't calm him. Ricardo changed his diaper, hoping this would make him more comfortable, but the crying did not stop. Ricardo took all of Ricky's clothes off to find out what was bothering him, and noticed his arm looked floppy and broken.

In a frightened tone, Ricardo exclaimed, "There is something wrong with his arm! We need to take him to the emergency room, right now!" Esperanza and Ricardo left the girls with their abuelito Antonio, who was living with them during this time, and rushed Ricky to the ER around the corner.

Dr. Davis attended to them, beginning by moving Ricky's arm around. This caused his face to turn purple from the irritation as Ricardo and Esperanza watched in distress.

"He's fine. It was just dislocated, but he's fine now," declared Dr. Davis, despite Ricky seeming far from fine.

"But he's still crying!" asserted Esperanza.

"Well, you're spoiling him! You have to let him cry sometimes. Everything is fine now. You can go."

"Can you please call our pediatrician before we go?" Esperanza was not convinced.

"I already did. She said he should be fine," argued Dr. Davis.

"Well, we are not leaving here without an X-ray, at least," said Ricardo sternly.

"Okay, fine! If you want to pay…" Dr. Davis said with a wise-guy attitude.

Ricardo looked at him with disdain as the doctor walked over to a colleague and loudly ridiculed the parents: "My gosh, these first-time parents! Always think they have to bring their kids to the emergency room for no reason." The nurses took the X-ray, put Ricky in a baby sling, and waited for the doctor to come back and explain the results.

"Mr. and Mrs. Rodriguez," Dr. Davis addressed the two parents as he walked toward them with an authoritarian look on his face. "I called the police. Your son has a spiral break, which can only be done by viciously twisting the arm."

Esperanza and Ricardo were shocked and furious.

"You were the one twisting Ricky's arm!" shouted Esperanza, reflexively. Frightened, she held Ricky, comforting him as much as she could. All of a sudden, two police officers arrived and asked Esperanza to hand Ricky over to them. The parents' faces twisted in disbelief.

"No!" Esperanza protested. Panic rushed over Ricardo while the police officers told them they needed to investigate both him and Esperanza because of Ricky's spiral break.

Horrified, Ricardo began explaining, "We did not do this! We just came back from dinner! Our kids were with our nanny. The doctor was the one twisting his arm!"

The officers separated Esperanza and Ricardo and demanded the couple tell their accounts of what happened. In one room, Esperanza held Ricky, while in the other Ricardo sat anxiously, rubbing the back of his neck and repeatedly clenching his jaw. The anxious parents both laid out the order of events as best they could, their anger mounting by the minute. The two police officers reconvened to discuss what they heard and found one major discrepancy between the spouses' stories.

Esperanza and Ricardo were then pulled into the same room.

"Sir, ma'am, we're taking your baby away from you."

Immediately, a chaotic spew of "What?! Wait a minute! Why?! No! You can't do that!" poured out of Esperanza and Ricardo.

"Yes, we can," the police officers said firmly.

Trying his best to deescalate the situation, Ricardo managed to convince one of the officers into going back to his and Esperanza's home to show them what kind of environment their kids lived in, hoping to persuade the officers into dropping the case.

Ricardo walked the police officers around the house, frantically narrating the home life he was so proud to have built. Back at the hospital, Esperanza nervously bounced Ricky to sleep in her arms as Ricardo and the officer returned. The officers told them there was still a discrepancy in their stories but would not explain what it was. They tried taking Ricky away again, but Esperanza cocooned him and would not let him go.

It was now just past midnight, and the officers were relentless, but Esperanza and Ricardo wouldn't compromise. A lot of discussion took place, and it persisted until almost five in the morning when the officers finally tore Ricky from Esperanza's arms. Screaming for their baby back, the parents grasped at the officers, fighting them with every breath, until the police drove away with their son. Esperanza and Ricardo fell to the ground, sobbing and wailing, unable to fathom how this was happening. Their baby boy was gone, and they had no clue where these men were taking him.

Separating families, especially children from their parents, in the absence of abuse, protects no one. It only causes grief and heartache. These individuals then hold onto this trauma, in their bodies and minds, and gradually it seeps into their world and communities, affecting us all in nebulous ways. Yes, I believe in the butterfly effect — also known as chaos theory — and I believe it is one of trauma's worst impacts. Ending its ripple requires open honesty, active listening and reparations. It requires breaking our silence.

Esperanza and Ricardo did not sleep a single wink that night. They were going out of their minds. Esperanza's body felt like it was missing half of itself, and yet, she felt heavier than ever. Together with her husband, she kicked into full detective mode, first calling the nanny. After hearing her account of what happened, the parents spoke with their two young daughters to piece the full story together.

According to the girls, Barbara left the three children alone in the living room while she was on the phone in the office. Amelia — two years old at the time — tried picking Ricky up out of the baby swing, and accidentally dropped him on the floor. Ricky was crying, so Valentina — four years old — picked him up and put him back in the baby swing. When Barbara came back into the living room, Ricky was no longer on the floor, but she had no reason to believe he was hurt. Esperanza and Ricardo had their story, and now they needed to get their baby.

Esperanza drove to the pediatrician's office, while Ricardo went to their family physician. The family physician was horrified when he learned what happened. He became furious, called the emergency room, and scolded Dr. Davis. He was willing to help Ricardo and his family in any way he could.

Upon arriving at the pediatrician, Esperanza learned Dr. Davis lied about calling the pediatrician the night before, giving Esperanza a glimpse of investigative empowerment. On her way out, one of the nurses mentioned the police likely took Ricky to a place called Orangewood Home — a place where children are taken when their parents abuse them. Esperanza and Ricardo met back up and immediately went to Orangewood, but were told they needed to speak to Ricky's case worker, Brad Miller, who wouldn't be back until Monday. It was Saturday, and the two parents were not willing to wait that long.

Esperanza and Ricardo raced home, grabbed the white pages, and immediately started calling everybody with the last name Miller. Finally, after what felt like hundreds of calls, they reached the right number.

"Hi, is Brad Miller, the case worker from Orangewood Home available?"

"No, but this is his mother. How can I help?"

Esperanza and Ricardo explained to Brad's mother the situation and were assured she would relay the message and have Brad give them a call as soon as possible. They felt close to victory.

No more than an hour later, the phone rang. Ricardo and Esperanza held high hopes it was Brad, but instead were greeted, rather apprehensively, by another representative from Orangewood Home. The woman sounded nervous as she quickly let Esperanza and Ricardo know Ricky's case was now a floating case. This meant nobody wanted to take it on, and the family would have to wait for someone new to be appointed to the case in order to move forward.

The representative relayed that Mr. Miller and others at the service center could not understand how the two parents got his phone number, going so far as to declare, "We're afraid. We don't know who we're dealing with. For all we know, you may be a part of a Mexican gang. How else were you able to get Brad's number?"

The ignorance. Esperanza was quick to explain how she and her husband simply called everybody in the white pages with that last name, but the officials made up a story to fit their fear-based racist narrative, and they were not changing it — even when the only true narrative was that a mother and father were desperate to reunite with their newborn child.

Making matters even more tense, Antonio, Ricardo's dad, wanted to take off to Mexico with Valentina and Amelia, fearing the "bad people" would come and take them away, too. Ricardo and Esperanza appreciated his intentions to keep the girls safe but knew that was not the solution. They kept a close eye on him, knowing his love for his granddaughters could easily compel him to drive them to the safety of Mexico without their permission.

After hanging up with Orangewood Home, Ricardo and Esperanza called the attorney that the family physician had referred them to. The attorney felt strongly that what was happening was not right and believed the parents were innocent. He made clear they could sue the county, the police department, and the hospital, but it would not be easy. And it would not happen overnight.

He warned: "It could take years and you will have to relive every single detail in front of a jury, and in front of a judge. But you have a remarkably strong case, and if you want to go through with a lawsuit, I am your guy. I will fight with you until the end."

It was now Monday, the third day since Ricky was taken from his family, and Ricardo and Esperanza's lawyer had excellent news: They could finally go see Ricky. Esperanza was desperate to nurse him, but she was not allowed by Orangewood Home for fear she may be drug addicted or otherwise dangerous. This crushed Esperanza's spirits. At every turn, her determination to provide her child with the unconditional love and support her own mother couldn't manage was rejected. The tightness in her chest intensified.

Ricky was at Orangewood Home for a total of five days before Esperanza and Ricardo were able to take him home, but the investigation against them continued. Every day for two weeks, a social worker by the name of Brigid came over to observe Esperanza interact with her children while Ricardo was at work. At the end of those two weeks, the two main investigators on the case came to the house to question four-year-old Valentina. The investigators handed Valentina a doll and asked her to tell them what happened. She walked them through the story, showing them what took place.

The investigators, still suspicious, turned to Ricardo and Esperanza and demanded they recount their stories yet again. Esperanza and Ricardo took turns recounting every detail they could, hoping to shed more light.

"We came home, and our live-in nanny went to my sister's house to babysit her kids for the night," said Ricardo.

"Yes, we came home, and our live-in nanny went to my brother's to babysit his kids for the night," stated Esperanza.

"Aha! I caught you again with the same lie!" exclaimed one of the investigators.

"What?!" asked Esperanza and Ricardo, utterly confused.

"You just lied to us! You said the nanny went with your brother, and you said she went with your sister!" The investigators were sure they'd finally caught their suspects red-handed.

Esperanza and Ricardo's blood boiled. Their brows furrowed as their faces morphed into pure outrage. Esperanza lost it.

"My brother is married to his sister!" she yelled.

The investigators were stunned.

"Are you telling me that is why our baby was taken away?!" Ricardo demanded to know.

The investigators looked at one another in a moment of shameful silence. "Well, yes," the investigators voiced in a low regretful tone. "That was the main discrepancy."

Esperanza burned with resentment and loudly pressed them, "Why did someone not tell us what the discrepancy was? Why did you not continue asking questions?!"

"We are so sorry," the investigators said guiltily.

"You mean to tell me if we did not speak a word of English, or have the resources available to us, that most likely our other two children would have been taken away from us, too?!" Esperanza hollered.

Embarrassed, the investigators conceded, explaining the likelihood given the status of Ricky's floating case, and the conspiring — and ludicrous — belief that Ricardo and Esperanza were part of a Mexican gang — otherwise gangsters themselves.

"You were told in the hospital by a social worker where your baby was going and what the steps were, and you did not follow them properly," one attempted.

"There was no social worker at the hospital!" Esperanza professed.

Yet again, the investigators were dumbfounded and embarrassed at the level of obvious negligence on their side. Apologizing profusely, they quickly realized Dr. Davis likely called the police to cover his own carelessness with Ricky. The investigators left, and the case was dropped.

Unsure of whether to proceed with a lawsuit, Esperanza and Ricardo spoke to their lawyer. Empathetic, he zeroed in on Esperanza.

"If you decide to move forward, I will take your case all the way. But I can tell you are not doing well. I want you to know that most of the time, healing begins after the case is over. This case will last for many years, because we will be going up against the police department, the hospital, and the county. If we win, you will get a lot of money, but you should think about your health first."

Ricardo exhaled deeply, "We already have Ricky back. That is all we wanted. Esperanza, I will leave it up to you whether you want to pursue the case or not."

The couple were both psychologically shattered, and wanted to restore peace in their home. Esperanza was losing control of her mental state, and it was not just the lack of sleep from her insomnia. She was not herself — zoning out for long periods of time, doing the same menial task over and over while she stared into a deep void. She perched herself on the sofa most of the day and rocked back and forth with Ricky in her arms. Neither Esperanza nor Ricky wanted to be away from one another. In fact, they were terrified of being apart.

Esperanza decided to drop the case, but was losing grasp of any positive thoughts. She was furious that her child was taken from her, an innocent and good mother, yet she was not taken away when she was a child from her parents, who were guilty of the gravest abuse. *Why was I not taken away? Why did nobody show up when I was little? Why did this happen to my baby?* These thoughts cycled through her mind, and the more she stewed on them the angrier she grew. Fury overwhelmed her brain and body. There was no justice. She was robbed as a child — of her innocence. And she was robbed now as a mother — of her child. She trusted nobody.

Even though the case was dropped, Brigid, the social worker, checked on Esperanza out of sheer kindness. She recognized how much Esperanza was struggling, and suggested she speak to a psychologist immediately.

Esperanza looked at Brigid with eyes of desperation and nodded in agreement. She knew what she needed to do if she were to survive this life. She needed to talk. So, she took Brigid's advice and saw her first psychologist at the age of 27. In the end, it was the trauma of having her son taken from her by the state that finally drove her to speak — for the first time — about the trauma of her childhood, and the barbaric life she lived with her father.

People tend to think we have no memories from our infancy, but that is not true. Our bodies remember. Imagine: a four-month-old baby living in isolation, away from everything they know, for five days. Imagine: a new mother, still breastfeeding, has her newborn ripped from her arms. Imagine: a new father, feeling powerless to bring his baby back home. It is unconscionable. It is unethical. It yanks you into a fiery rage before thrusting you further down into the depths of your darkest abyss, leaving a deep scar.

Sometimes I wonder, as my dad did before me, if racism was at the root of the outrageously improper handling of my family's case. Afterall, it was the 80s and we were a Mexican family living in the United States under Ronald Reagan. Regardless, this event rattled my mom so profoundly that it marked a critical turning point in her life: She accepted her need for therapy. Drowning deep in the dark waters of her past and present, surrendering herself to the voids vastness, she reached up. Therapy was the first vital step on her path to opening up, letting go, and grabbing onto the light.

14

The more Esperanza spoke the repulsive and barbaric truth about her relationship with her father aloud, the more relief she felt. And slowly, over weeks of strenuous therapy sessions, her relief began transforming to clarity and courage. It was her psychologist who prompted her to begin writing, and thus her Garfield Journal, where she finally took pen to paper and wrote her story in devastating detail, was born.

One of Esperanza's first assignments was to tell her brothers about this dark secret. Her psychologist, Maya, knew it was an essential step in reclaiming herself, and Esperanza knew she was right. With no idea about the abuse that took place in their childhood home, her brothers admired their parents, aiming to live up to the standard they set. It needed to shatter, and soon.

Before sharing the devastating abuse with her brothers, Esperanza decided to tell her mom that she was planning on it. Carmen's response was upsettingly oppressive: "No! What will they think of you?!"

Esperanza's eyes widened as she heard this come out of her mother's mouth. It wasn't just foolish, it was shameful, deeply rooted in culture of victim-blaming.

Esperanza upped the ante of her own healing, going from therapy once a week, to twice a week. Therapy was expensive — as it still is now — but Esperanza and Ricardo scraped together the hundred dollars per hour to help her manage her trauma. With Maya's assistance, Esperanza planned out the first emergency meeting with her brothers. First, she made reservations for her parents to spend a weekend in Las Vegas and gave it to them as a Christmas gift — albeit with ulterior motives. With her parents out of town, it was time for her to tell her brothers.

The first Friday of January, 1990, Esperanza phoned each of her brothers, calling for a family meeting at her house the next morning, without the spouses. She did not want to give them too much time to wonder, concerned about how they would react. Esperanza and her four brothers had until then known their parents to be totally different people. She was worried they would not believe her, or that one of them would want to harm their father — another reason for sending their parents out of town.

The next morning, Ricardo took Valentina and Amelia to the park to give Esperanza the space he knew she needed, while Ricky slept soundly at home in his crib. At the park, Ricardo relaxed, reclining on the grass, lovingly observing his daughters become immersed in the freedom of endless blue and white sky. Soft breezes whispered through the sisters' curls as they ran through the open field, birds scattering from the grass into the boundless sky, seeming so close within reach of their little hands. Laughing and discovering a life of dreams pure and true, Valentina and Amelia soaked in the brightness of the day, while soft, sweet melodies played from the mobile spinning over Ricky's head at home.

One by one, the brothers filed into the house. Leo arrived in his big wheeled, souped-up Toyota truck, walking in tall with a clean haircut, thin mustache, and brown eyes softening his strong male energy. Fernando was next, his afro entered first, then his thick mustache, then finally that loud yet loving voice. Samuel followed, nervous yet calm, leading with his broad shoulders, strong jaw, and an overall clean-cut presentation. Daniel's arrival was heard by all as he drove up in his black 280Z, blaring Pink Floyd. More nervous than the rest, with his clean-shaven baby face and shoulder-length dark brown curly hair, he was the last to file in.

The siblings embraced one another and took their places in the family room, with no idea the earth was about to split from under their feet.

Esperanza sat nervously, rubbing her hands against her thighs and shifting in her seat on the couch. Her brothers stared at her, waiting for their sister to speak.

"I know it may be hard to believe what I am about to share," she began, "because Mom and Dad have always been really good to you. But they have been totally different with me, and you need to know this."

She took a deep breath, exhaling loudly.

"Since the time I was a child, Dad has sexually, physically and mentally abused me."

She took a big gulp and looked on anxiously at her brothers' confused and shocked expressions, allowing their speechlessness to be her stage as she contextualized her thoughts and spared them the gruesome details. She turned to Fernando and asked if he remembered the incident when she was five and he told her he would run away if Dad touched her again, but he could not remember. She tried to refresh his memory, but he blocked it out completely. I would have, too. No one, especially a ten-year-old child should have to witness that kind of body-freezing trauma.

She disclosed to her brothers how their mother would force her to take dinner to their father in the master bedroom, knowing he was nude, waiting to molest her. And how she was forced to give him massages while he wore only underwear. And how she was forced to take the nannies to the master bedroom window to watch their parents having sex. And how when their father walked around the house at night nude, he was going in and out of her bedroom to violate her — all throughout their childhood.

Esperanza thought how staggering it must be for her brothers to learn that their father was not who they thought he was. She could see it in their distraught, beady eyes. They could not fully grasp what they were hearing, and it was hard for them to accept. They were utterly baffled. As the siblings sat in the sanctuary of their own company, the quiet stormed in and became deafening, until Daniel suddenly broke out crying endlessly.

"I witnessed it!" he cried out. "She is telling the truth! I am so sorry, Esperanza, I knew! I have witnessed it. There was a lot of physical and mental abuse towards me, too, because Dad knew I knew. Once, he stopped talking to me for an entire year."

Fernando, Samuel, and Leo could not believe what they were hearing. They could not understand how they would not have caught on. They sat with the weight of it, incredulous and uncomfortable.

"No! There's just no way!" the three brothers pleaded helplessly, hoping this was somehow all a twisted joke.

Esperanza felt her own sense of shock as she stared at Daniel with love and sadness in her eyes, learning for the first time about his own traumatic upbringing that she also never caught onto. Daniel lived a tortured life because of what he knew. Their father did not want him to say a word about his evil deeds, so he beat him senseless. Esperanza grabbed his hand.

"I believe you," she said into his eyes before turning to the other three. "As I grew, I was able to fight Dad off, and because of that he would stop talking to me for a month at a time. That was my punishment, I guess. He would completely ignore me, even though he would still try to molest me. He tried to make me feel even smaller, like I was nobody. Not only was I abused, I did not *exist*. He erased me."

Daniel, talking through the tears, shared more about what he witnessed as a little boy. "It got to the point where I would fearfully be watching to see what Dad was doing to you, Esperanza, and he knew I was watching and didn't even care."

Slowly, the truth sank in for the others and Fernando, Samuel, and Leo became furious. Esperanza and Daniel said more than anyone wanted to hear. The three brothers asked no questions — they did not need to after Daniel's impassioned confirmation. All of the brothers' questions were being answered right there. Esperanza escalated the discussion.

"I want to press charges. I've been doing research and looked into an attorney. The best attorney I could find is this lady Gloria Allred."

The three brothers collectively became nervous. Having just found out the truth about their father with little time to process, they pleaded: "Please! Please, do not press charges! Not yet."

Esperanza let her brothers' pleas sit with her. She thought about how long it had been since he last touched her. She thought about how she just flipped her brothers' worlds upside down. She recognized that the time to prosecute her father likely had already passed. Respecting her brothers' wishes, she did not go through with pressing charges.

For hours, the five siblings talked, listened, and cried. They hugged and held space for one another as Esperanza told them she did not want their parents in their lives anymore. Three of them now knew their parents as they never did before. Samuel was fuming, becoming more enraged with every passing second. He cried and loudly cursed, promising he was going to beat the hell out of their dad. Knowing one of them would react this way, Esperanza let her brothers know she sent their parents out of town so they could process this news without them around.

Hector and Carmen, none the wiser, strolled the lit-up streets of Las Vegas, eating, gambling, and enjoying themselves as their children learned their darkest secret and the gut-wrenching truth that would change all of their lives forever.

Back at the park, Ricardo gathered his daughters and made their way back home. He circled the block to make sure all his brothers-in-law's cars were gone, and pulled into the driveway, nervous about the next time he would see them. Things would be different from this day forward.

As an adult, I was curious how big of a turning point this was for my family. My dad offered transparency.

"Your mom and I never really talked much about it," he said, "so when we got back from the park, we discussed the emergency meeting only briefly.

"Back then it was so, hush hush and I still did not want to know the details of the abuse — wrongfully so, because it was part of my wife's life. We should have coped with it together, but that did not happen properly for a while. I did not discuss it with any of your mom's brothers afterwards, either. I thought I would wait and see if any of them approached me about it, but nothing. None of them ever mentioned it to me, and I did not mention anything to them. I am pretty sure, once your abuelitos got back from Vegas, your tíos did not speak to them about it at all."

It is easy to look back at life and know what you would do differently, but it can feel all sorts of complicated to pull yourself into the present, understand what needs to be done, and do it.

During this time the family needed to have discussions, and though the conversations began, they were hard for everyone. The evil that surrounded us came in dark flashes amidst an otherwise bright and joyful life, confusing all who reckoned with it. My mom's brothers were still in shock as they entered their first stage of grief: denial.

Before long, their brains were speeding between anger, bargaining, denial, depression, and acceptance, as bit by bit, my tíos lost the perception of the people they thought were their mother and father. But slowly, they buried the topic deep enough in their minds that it almost disappeared, as they struggled to grasp for normalcy.

This first emergency meeting revealed hard family truths to all five siblings, including my mom. That was the first time she found out her youngest brother knew about the sexual abuse and was beaten severely and regularly for it. Shortly after the meeting, Tío Daniel wrote my mom a letter and asked her to read it in private.

She shared with me how she drove to what she called her 'safe space,' pulled out a perfectly folded letter with perfect penmanship, in dark, black ink, and read:

Esperanza, I guess the first time I realized what was going on was when I was about nine. I was outside Mom and Dad's bedroom and I heard you say, "No Apa! Don't touch me there!" You remember what a snoop I was then, so of course I got closer to listen. I never dreamed what I heard would haunt me for the rest of my life. I could not believe what was going on. Here was a girl who we were to treat like a princess and my dad was touching you, making you cry and touch him. I could not understand this. I could not believe how our father could do such a thing. I ran to the living room and tried to pretend like nothing was going on. Esperanza, I've never been so scared in all my life than when Dad finally came out of the room and into the living room. He looked over at me and knew at that instant that I had heard and realized what happened. Esperanza, he took me outside to the backyard and asked me, "What were you doing outside my room?!" I lied. I told him I was in the living room. He called me "Liar!" Esperanza, that was the first time he beat me. He told me it was because I lied and was listening and snooping around his room. When he sent me to my room I was horrified, because I knew the beating was not because I lied or was snooping. It was because Dad was doing something very bad and he wanted me to know what would happen if I ever said anything. From then on out, I feared Dad like he was the devil himself.

Time went on and it got worse. I'm sure more for you than me. He would drink and do those things to you and not care that I was around, because when I was around, the same thing would happen. He would tell me I did wrong and beat me. Esperanza, I heard and saw many of the things that he did to you. You know, the worst thing about it is, he hurt you and your begging and crying for him to stop is imbedded in my mind. Esperanza, I remember in detail every time I heard or saw what happened to you and what he would do to me because I snooped. Like you Esperanza, I have many years of horrible memories from our father. You know, when Ricardo asked you to marry him, I was so relieved, because here was this man who was going to take you away from the devil who would call you a whore and punish you because Ricardo would put his hands on you. When the bastard himself had actually done these things to you.

After you had left for college, it seemed like day after day he would find a reason, so he said, to punish me for screwing up. Esperanza, he was drunk one time and I swear to you he beat me and bruised my ribs for leaving soap bubbles on the sponge in the shower. The man needed no reason to take his aggressions out on me. He would just use any excuse he possibly could. Esperanza, you know what was weird after a while? I expected the pain and the punishment and it no longer hurt. He would hit me and I would stand there and not flinch. He would get furious and hit me because now I was being a smartass, he would say. He actually accused me of making fun of him because I no longer showed fear or pain in his presence. To this very day, I hate him for giving me the ability to show no emotion or pain when I choose.

The last day he beat me was when I was 18. He hit me and I put a knife to my throat and asked him to just kill me because if he continued, I promised him I would. I could not believe what happened. Esperanza, the devil cried to me and said, 'I'm sorry.' We both lived through quite the horror story of a childhood. I guess that's why I turned out the freak of the family. God only knows how you turned out to be such a beautiful person. Esperanza, I love you very much. I wrote you this letter because I need you to know how proud I am of you, and will always support any decision in your life and to let you know Esperanza, I am very sorry I have let this happen to you and never went for help. I've never known such pain to know that you lived the horrible memories I do. Esperanza, please forgive me.

    Love Daniel.

15

Reading the letter aloud to me, my mom bared her soul in a powerful fit of tears and emotion. We wept, sniffling back snot as she finished reading Tío Daniel's words. She was distraught.

"This was a little nine-year-old! When you think of a child and how he used to get beat, it's awful. He was such a little guy, and went through hell."

Our sobbing went on, like a river flowing from our hearts, cascading from our eyes. My body was in brutalizing distress. I wanted to curl up in the fetal position and calm myself to stillness. But I couldn't. I owed my mom this chance to share her story. To be heard.

"When Tío Daniel was older and lived downtown," my mom went on, "he could not sleep. He would hear my voice screaming for help and would run to the window, certain I was there. He was having hallucinations all the time and would remember everything. Even in sleep, he could not escape. This lasted years.

"This is what upsets me the most. My being abused was one thing, because I learned to live with it, but to see how it crucified Daniel and how it affected others was in some ways worse. It was always in my life, so I learned to manage it from a young age, but not everybody could. Some people really got screwed up from everything, and Daniel was one of them. There was a reason he started sniffing glue at nine years old."

My mom's voice started to shake, and it took all her energy not to erupt, "It was not like Daniel waited until he was older. He started in elementary school! Why does a little kid in elementary school start doing drugs? There is a reason! He wanted to escape everything!"

Tears rolled down both our faces and I felt, once again, as if my body was floating. I felt like I was in a dream, my connection to my body disappearing with every line of my mother's story. I thought about Tío Daniel, trapped in a dark cycle of disturbing images, horrifying cries, and severe beatings through his formative years. I closed my eyes to breathe and wrap him in love. He paid the unfair price for knowing his father's darkest sins. As a nine-year-old child, how do you reconcile the man who is supposed to be your hero, beating you until you bruise, and your bones become brittle? History was repeating itself. This ferocious way of fathering a nine-year-old son was passed down to yet another generation, but Tío Daniel broke the cycle, drowning himself in his traumas rather than inflicting pain on others the way his Abuelito and father did.

Tio Daniel was a keeper of the family's trauma — and the hidden healer that would help many of us along our path for years to come.

"Daniel was five years younger than me and always looked up to me like I was more than an older sister. He looked to me for guidance," my mom said proudly. "I did not always know why, but I found out during the first emergency meeting. He used to tell me I was more of a mother figure to him than our own mother. He was always a huge support for me, and our relationship was different after we told each other our truths.

"We were the only two who understood the extent of our parents' destruction. I was the one, out of all the siblings, who could be real with Daniel, and he would actually stop and listen. We went through similar realities. My other brothers' never knew our father that way, so it was hard for them to truly comprehend. Imagine all of a sudden waking up one day as an adult and realizing your parents are not the people you thought they were. That is terrifying," she said sympathetically.

I felt as if my heart was clenched in a fist, squeezing tight, making it hard to breathe. A wall of stillness formed around us as we stared at each other. It was time to openly acknowledge the impact of the anguish. Knowing we were safe and in cherished company allowed for comfortable silence. We were fixed in the present with emotions of the past. I thought of my tíos, and what this news must have done to their minds, bodies, and souls.

My tíos and my mother, special in their own ways, are the ones most intensely affected by the ripple effects of my grandfather's sins and my grandmother's non-existent will to fight for her children and grandchildren. When I look back at old pictures of my mom and tíos, beautiful and handsome, I see past their hurt. I see them. I see their white light, their personalities and spirits of love for life. They are much more than the pain their parents caused. They are not their mother. They are not their father. They are them, and they are glorious. Glorious enough to have brung forth a new generation who is mindful and connected to higher levels of consciousness in our own ways — learning to be mindful in our thoughts and actions and be present as often as we can.

My heart wide open and full of compassion, I revived this conversation with Tío Leo, the second youngest of my mom's siblings, after it lay dormant for too long.

"I did not see anything that would lead me to believe something bad was going on," stated Tío Leo. "We seemed like a normal family. Everyone looked up to my dad and we had a lot of fun times as kids. We did not have a lot of money and yet we were still getting out, camping, and doing a lot of gathering as a family.

"That was my perception as a kid, anyway. Daniel always had kind of a troublesome childhood, but I did not think much of it back then. I remember him sniffing glue a lot. Thinking back, there was definitely something bothering him, because as a kid, who thinks of that? When I was about ten years old, Daniel and I would sleep in the living room and I would see my dad walking around at night, coming in and out of doors, naked."

He paused before stating his next thoughts. "He was probably going into my sister's room. But as a kid, you don't think of that. You reflect later in life and find out what was truly going on, and it all makes sense. I did not know until your mom told us at the first emergency meeting."

Change was in motion, although gradual, ever since that first meeting. My tíos were stunned by the revelation of secrets so dark and evil, the brothers, submerged in their muted cries and screams. Soon, my tíos began drowning in their own silence as they wished and hoped for a better ending, one that did not end with their father as a pedophile and their mother as his enabler. But there was no other reality. My tíos would come to these terms on their own time, as all trauma survivors must do.

I stared warmly at tío Leo thinking of my mom's words, "My brothers worlds were flipped upside down. And they have been ever since. My siblings and I were some of the ones most gravely affected by my parents' actions. We had to stop this. We needed to start somewhere, and in that first emergency meeting, we decided we were the generation who needed to begin the healing. We knew it would not be easy, but we were going to do something about it. I was determined. I wasn't sure how I was going to put a stop to it, but I knew I had to."

Silence Ends

16

Two years after the first emergency meeting, Abuelito Hector and Abuelita Carmen still reigned as the leaders of our family. For my tíos, the shell-shock and shame of their parents' actions kept them from confronting their parents and telling their wives. In order to escape their ugly reality, they had only one coping mechanism: dissociation.

Although from the outside life seemed to continue as normal, the internal lives of my mom and her brothers were never the same, the burden of this secret too great to bear. Her brothers lived in deep denial. No one denied the truth of what happened, but the brothers desperately suppressed their trauma, until they were ready to dig it up and make sense of it. Feelings of fear, angst, happiness, confusion, love, and deep sadness colored these years, trickling down through the adults to us children.

The Madero patriarch was fatally flawed, deeply troubled, and the rot of his evil was permeating. How does a family rebuild when the men are all broken? How does a family rebuild when most of the women are kept in the dark, plagued by secrecy? How does one function with any semblance of normalcy when much of what you thought you knew was a lie?

And yet, our family was still standing, laughing, dancing, as the children of my generation brought a glimmer of hope that would help break the chains of tortured silence.

In December of 2018, my sister and I sat together in an RV parked on the side of her home as the evening settled upon us. We sipped our wine while my nephew — her four-year-old son — entertained us. His presence alone brought me joy. He jumped around asking questions about what we were doing. I answered him truthfully, without giving him unnecessary details, allowing him to be happy with my answer. "I'm writing a book on Abuelita's life, and Ma is going to share some stories with me for the book," I said with a big grin on my face.

We never lied to him, knowing full well the best way to respect a child was to speak the truth, no matter what. We knew what lies and secrets could do to a family, and we were committed to bringing honesty through our future generations. With a big smile on my face, I scooped him up in my arms, gave him a big hug and kiss goodnight before my brother-in-law swept him off to bed, giving my sister and I our space to talk.

Valentina put her legs up on the couch, a firm grip on her glass. She stared at me with her glowing green eyes that she must have got from Abuelita Elena, and her long brown hair. Taking a sip of her Bordeaux, she prepared to divulge.

"I was eight years old," said Valentina. "I was in the backseat of the car and Mami was driving me to my best friend's house for a slumber party. It was the first time I was going to spend the night away from home, and I was excited. As we drove, we listened to oldies music from the 60s and Mami started telling me not to ever let anyone touch me, and if anyone ever did, to scream and immediately tell her or Papi about it.

"She was nervous about letting me stay the night somewhere, and that prompted her to ask me 'Has anyone ever touched you?' I hesitated to answer because I was not sure if I did something wrong, but I replied, 'Yes. Abuelito.' A rush of fear washed over her and I immediately knew something about it was wrong. She asked me 'which abuelito?'

"I told her 'Abuelito Hector.'"

My mom had shared with me the enormous guilt she was instantly slammed with hearing her oldest daughter confirm her worst nightmare. The vines from her internal hell wound around her, taking tight hold of every inch of her body, slowly creeping into every cell, wrapping around every thought in her mind.

I shut my eyes and channeled the love between my sister and I. As I listened to her share the story I heard several times throughout the years, a coldness ran through my body. Valentina took a deep breath and continued.

"I started telling her about how Abuelito Hector molested me, and she slowed the car down to a crawl, circling and circling the same neighborhood. I told her in as much detail as I could remember. The first time was in the bathroom of his house, but I do not remember that time well. This other incident, at our house, I remember clearly.

"It was Christmas Eve and we were all in the living room. You and I were wearing matching poofy dresses, and Abuelito called me over to sit on his lap, so I did. Abuelita Carmen was next to us and it was loud, like

Christmas Eve loud. People were having fun, talking, eating, drinking, dancing, playing, just enjoying each other. All of a sudden, he started touching me from underneath my dress with everybody in the room.

"I remember thinking, *Why is this happening again?* I was really confused, especially because it was so nonchalant in front of so many people. I thought, *This does not feel good, but is it bad? Is it good? If it was bad, Mami and Papi would not have me here.* You can imagine how confusing this would be for a young child. I pretended to hear Mami call my name and I told Abuelito Hector, 'Oh, my mom needs me,' and I hopped off his lap and scurried into the kitchen saying, 'What? Mami? Did you need something? Here, let me help you,' and I started helping with whatever she was doing. When I told her this in the car, the circling and quiet confirmed this was bad. Very bad."

Valentina and I allowed the heater to soothe our goosebumps. She continued to share her 8-year-old thoughts with me about the thunderous silence in the car that day.

"I thought, *Oh no! Is she not going to let me spend the night at Cathy's house?* That was the big concern on my mind. Mami said she did not want me to feel like I was in trouble, and still took me to Cathy's house to spend the night. When we walked into their house, Mami and Cathy's mom went into a different room to talk. After Mami left, we watched a movie about touching and telling. Years later I found out Mami told Cathy's mom what happened, and that VHS was at their house because Cathy's mom was also a survivor of sexual abuse. That was the first and last time I spent the night at anybody's house for a really long time."

My sister and I laughed, thinking about all the times we heard the word "No" when begging to spend the night anywhere.

My mom was already struggling to manage her own trauma at this time, and Valentina's disclosure was exacerbating. I shared with my sister how our mom disclosed to me that as much as she wanted to help my sister through the trauma that lay ahead, she and our dad knew that they would not be enough, so they decided to get Valentina into a private Catholic school. My parents hoped it would give Valentina an additional community to lean on, as the convent had for my mother in her youth.

My sister laughed with a knowing look on her face. "Funny enough, my friends from there have become my strongest community to date, helping me through many stages of my trauma." We shared a smile and deep gratitude for my parents.

❧

The day after Valentina's terrifying reveal, there was a cousin's birthday party to attend. Esperanza did not want to go because her father would be there. Begrudgingly, Esperanza decided to go to the party. In her father's sinister presence, the last thing she wanted was for her kids to attend the party without her watchful eye to protect them. Plus, she still needed to speak to Ricardo and her brothers. Her absence would likely cause suspicion and would certainly raise eyebrows. Once at the party, angry and frantic, she pulled her sisters-in-law aside, one by one.

Esperanza did not share any details with them about Valentina's story, but assumed her brothers told their wives about what Hector did to her and Daniel as kids. Esperanza communicated to each of them that she needed to have a second emergency meeting with her brothers the following morning, alone — she had more bad news about their father. She asked the women to tell their husbands to arrive early in the morning, hide any rifles in their home, and promised she would tell them everything after.

Esperanza's sisters-in-law looked at her confused but agreed. It was then that Esperanza realized not all her brothers told their wives what they learned during the first emergency meeting. Gloria knew, Fernando's wife, but it was apparent Jessica and Emma, Samuel and Leo's wives, had no idea.

The sisters-in-law were receiving what seemed like coded messages from Esperanza. The women re-entered the party and looked around, smiling on the outside but feeling deeply uneasy. As their eyes settled on Hector, in his natural state of drinking a beer, a dark curiosity came over them. Equally as ignorant as he was to the impending cataclysm, they would soon know the nature of his evil — before he knew his secret was out.

Hard as it was for Esperanza to attend that birthday party, she worried more for Valentina. She thought of how puzzling it had to be for her daughter to go to the birthday party with this monster. It had to end. She needed to end it. But she had to be smart about it.

❧

From the RV, Valentina dug for the memory of that day.

"I forget a lot of what happened, but as you mention details, memories start to awaken.

"For example, I always remembered the birthday party as a strange day, but in my head it was connected to absolutely nothing. Now I understand its significance. It feels gratifying to know how it developed, and to know I was a part of the change. But at the same time, it was very confusing. I was not taken to therapy nor was I explained or talked to about the situation. I felt kept in the dark as a child. I don't think Mami or Papi even realized therapy was an option for a kid at the time.

"As an adult, who has now gone to therapy, I don't blame them. I don't even blame Abuelito or Abuelita. If our abuelitos want to take responsibility for what they did, that is for them to handle. I can only manage myself, and I choose the road to a healthy, happy life. I choose forgiveness. The truth will set you free, and Mami helped us all get there."

I felt a quiver of validity run down my spine and capture my heart. The truth will set you free. This statement always makes me smile. It encapsulates my belief in the power of breaking silence.

"Anyway, Mami was shocked when I told her, yet there we were again, with Abuelito Hector, at another big party. I was watching all the kids running around having fun while I sat there, disoriented. I was always a mellow kid, but there was a point in my childhood, after the abuse, where I went inward. I actually stopped talking for a long time.

"So, there I was seated in the playroom, and one of our cousins was trying to show me his baseball card collection. I heard him say the first word, then everything became muffled. All noises were meshing together, like a big blob of sound. I slowly picked my head up and saw everything in slow motion. I thought, *What's happening?*

"I sensed something, but I did not know what. I snapped out of it when our cousin said, 'Did you hear what I said?! This baseball card is a really big deal and I have it!'

"I said, 'Cool, cool,' and nodded my head, trying to act composed, but looking back I was clearly distracted by greater concerns."

Esperanza, having not yet told Ricardo what happened to Valentina, started strategizing. This time, much quicker than the first time around. The birthday party ended, the sisters-in-law were warned, and the men would soon receive the horrific news. The whole ride home, Esperanza nervously prepared how she would tell Ricardo and her brothers, bracing herself for frenzied reactions. The family arrived home with three kids asleep in the car. Ricardo picked his children up, one by one, and took them to their beds. After putting the last kid to sleep, he walked down the stairs as Esperanza stood anxiously at the bottom.

"Ricardo, I need to talk to you," she said.

He looked at her and instantly became nervous by her tone. Not knowing what to expect, he followed her to the family room. Esperanza took a deep breath, revealing her conversation with Valentina on the way to Cathy's house.

"I was telling Valentina not to ever let anyone touch her, and if anyone ever tried, to scream. I asked her if anyone had ever touched her, and Ricardo...she said yes."

His face turned white with disbelief. His eyes went stone cold with shock as he stared at his wife, his breath becoming rapid and short. Time slowed down, and as Esperanza finished, life came to a screeching halt.

"I asked her who touched her and she told me it was her abuelito. Ricardo, it was my dad."

He remained paralyzed, staring. Esperanza felt his shock. The icy feeling in his body quickly turned to a burning fire of rage. The color came back into his face and he exploded with animosity as he sobbed. In between crying and the breaths that saved him from drowning, he thought, *I have to kill this man.*

"I'm going to shoot him!" he roared, furiously. Someone touched his little girl, and he wanted the monster to pay with his life. The urge to kill crept through his body, allowing his mind to wander to the valley of the shadow of death.

Esperanza understood his rage and anticipated this reaction, hence hiding his hunting rifle earlier that day. She looked at him and calmly yet firmly replied, "You cannot do that. You have to think. You have three kids. If you attack him, you will end up in jail." She told him her brothers were coming over the next morning to receive the news.

The two sat for a bit longer while Ricardo cried, shouting angrily about his father-in-law, and trying to catch his breath. Esperanza soothed him as much as she could and the couple retreated upstairs, feeling defeated. They peaked their heads into all three childrens' bedrooms, finally making their way to their own, falling asleep still in their clothes from that day, awaiting the next morning.

The Rodriguez household was up bright and early. With three kids in the house, there was no chance of sleeping past 6:30 a.m. Esperanza and Ricardo were early birds anyhow — Ricardo had been getting up at five a.m. since he was a kid to help his dad tend to the chickens, cows, and pigs in Purepero, while Esperanza was used to getting little sleep, having developed severe insomnia during childhood as a survival tactic. With her brothers not set to arrive until 10:30, Esperanza and Ricardo had some time to compose their mental state before opening themselves up to another explosive reaction from her brothers. Still, she was feeling a bit less nervous after sharing with her husband.

Ricardo walked to the backyard, into the gazebo, and started pacing back and forth. He did not know exactly what he was thinking of doing. He knew he wanted to end Hector's life, but he was not sure how. His mind ran wild with guilt and anger. He could not believe he and Esperanza allowed this man to stay in their lives and felt there was no one to blame but himself. Esperanza knew her husband was struggling and told him to stay in the backyard while she welcomed her brothers who were arriving.

Her brothers crossed the threshold of the front door and took their places in the living room once again. Esperanza proceeded to tell them exactly what Valentina shared with her, in as much detail as possible, letting her brothers know their father was no longer allowed in her or her children's lives. She watched as her brothers' faces dropped into grief-stricken bafflement. She was frank with her brothers: This time around her mind was made up — their father was out.

She went on to tell them she had spoken with each of their wives, that they now knew some of what was going on but was not sure exactly how much. Esperanza realized her brothers had still not processed the information from the first emergency meeting, but needed them to grasp reality faster. They discussed how they thought it stopped with Esperanza, but it clearly did not. Their father had to be stopped. And while they acknowledged it would be hard for their children's generation, they knew their own would be the one to suffer most.

Angry and destroyed, the brothers got up and walked to the backyard to find Ricardo wiping an endless flow of tears from his face. He looked up at them, "I'm sorry, but I may end up in prison. I don't think the man you call a father deserves to live. I need to kill him."

The brothers, also distraught, put their hands on Ricardo's shoulders. "Let's go for a hike," suggested Samuel.

Before the men could get on their way, Esperanza stopped Leo and pulled him aside. "Leo, I need you to come with me to confront Mom and Dad tomorrow. I need your support. I'm afraid of what the other four will do if they come with me."

Leo looked at his sister with watery eyes, pain radiating from his core, and assured her he would be there. He gave her a long hug and walked out the front door to join his fellow brothers in grief and frenzy. Daniel stayed behind with his sister while the rest ushered Ricardo into the backseat of Fernando's car where he slouched against the window, head in his hands.

"Where are you taking me?" he asked.

"Away from here for the day. We have to get out of Fountain Valley," Fernando directed.

Ricardo's face was that of a tortured man, as he thought, *You just want me out of here so I don't kill your father.* And as enraged as Esperanza's brothers were, killing their father was an extreme they were not willing to accept. The men drove for nearly an hour before reaching the trailhead. Pulling into the parking space, Ricardo did not want to get out of the truck, feeling the sudden urge to turn around and go back home.

"No, no. Let's just go back home. Why did you bring me here? I need to go home and be with my family!" he protested.

Fernando empathized with Ricardo and helped talk him down, "You don't want to go back home just yet. That's not a good idea. Let's start walking."

The four men, desperate to ease their suffering, walked and walked, losing sight of the trail, finding themselves in uncharted territory. They cleared a walking path for themselves, flattening bushes, and ripping apart plants obstructing their way. The sun beat down, creating beads of sweat that rolled down their faces and mixed with their tears. Two and a half hours in and the men were tired. Fernando encouraged them along, "Let's keep on going, guys! Let's get to the top. We're almost there."

Finally, the men reached the summit, and the weeping that accompanied their hike broke with profane exasperation. Samuel sobbed harder than the rest, "I can't believe my father did this! I can't believe he's my father!"

Fernando sat on a rock staring quietly out into the distance, sniffing back his cries. Leo was showing himself to be the most level-headed indeed, not sugar-coating his words, but speaking with clarity while he cried, "This is not us! He is a worthless human being with real problems. He should not be a father, but he is. No human being should ever do what he has done. This is not who we are!"

Ricardo vigorously rubbed the back of his neck and shouted, "I still want to kill him! I want to take his life. I don't know how, but I need to do something. This is not right!" For the next two hours, the men shouted, getting what they could off their chests before trekking back down the mountain. They drove home without speaking a word, dropping Ricardo off first. With the summer sun still offering a layer of light across the evening sky, Ricardo felt a twinge of gratitude creeping in, eager to get inside and be with his family. He opened the front door and was immediately greeted by the melodious sounds of his children.

In hindsight, my dad was glad he never went through with killing his father-in-law. "If I would have killed your abuelito Hector," he started, "I would have been just as bad as he was. Thinking and doing are two very different things. When you're upset, your thinking is clouded. You imagine doing something you would never do in your right mind. Even though it felt like the right thing to do, it would have only created more damage for the people I was trying to protect. Killing him would have been a selfish act."

The next day, Leo picked his sister up and they drove to their parents' house. Esperanza wanted to speak to their mother before their father arrived home from work. When the brother and sister arrived, they gathered with their mom in the family room and Esperanza wasted no time. She asked why — why was he like this? Why did Carmen allow him to go on behaving this way? And she revealed that now Valentina, too, had been molested by their father. Leo was silent, never taking his eyes off his mother. Carmen looked between her daughter and her son with a worried face — worried that the secret she'd worked her life to keep was getting out.

Esperanza, seeing her mother as a victim, and desperate to keep one of her parents in her life, offered an olive branch. "Mom, I spoke to Ricardo and he agreed you are welcome to come live with us, away from Dad. We'll even build you your own beautiful room and bathroom. You can be around your children and your grandchildren. Do you want to come live with us?"

Carmen did not know what to say and remained silent with a look of fear and desperation on her aging face. Esperanza, hurt and frustrated by her mom's non-responsiveness, replied, "We are waiting for Dad to get home to talk to him, too." The three of them didn't budge until the garage door opened, signaling Hector's arrival. Esperanza and Leo stood up and darted for the garage before their father entered the house.

Hector stepped out of his car with a smile and greeted his children, but Esperanza made room for no pleasantries. She cut him off with conviction. "I know. Valentina told me. You are never allowed to see my kids again. I never want to talk to you or see you ever again. Our relationship is over! This is where my silence ends."

She stood strong, staring at her father, furious inside, outwardly stern and poised. No tears at all. She felt a shift within, realizing she was a force he could no longer reckon with. She saw her father's angry expression quickly turn to worry, proving he felt her shift as well. Despite his attempts at minimizing her self-worth, she was a strong and powerful woman. Hector's eyes shifted from his daughter to his son. His fear that any of his boys would learn the horrible side of who he really was now realized. Stunned, he tried and failed to defend himself.

The hard truth was confirmed for Leo. This was goodbye. Esperanza had finally seized her father's strength, rendering him powerless over her. Hector stood motionless, suddenly appearing pitiful. Leo and Esperanza walked out of the garage, got in their car and drove away without looking back.

Esperanza was done with her father… or so she thought.

I thought I was done
Towards the end of my run
But life's got a way
To stand up and say
Your battle's just begun
So take your handgun
Raise it up in the air
Turn it to a fist and swear,
I'll kill you with kindness, I'll kill you with love
You ain't here to destroy me, cuz my center is love

Abuelita Elena Sanchez Valenzuela, soon after getting married. She passed away at 106 years old which means I got to spend 26 years with her. I can feel her strong spirit when I look at this picture.

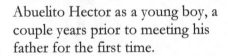

Abuelito Hector as a young boy, a couple years prior to meeting his father for the first time.

Abuelita Carmen Montel Madero in Purepero, Michoacán standing in front of an adobe home during her teenage years.

Abuelita Carmen Montel Madero soon after getting married. She was always known for her bold style.

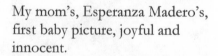

My mom's, Esperanza Madero's, first baby picture, joyful and innocent.

My mom, Esperanza, and Tío Fernando on her 1st birthday in 1962.

This is right around my mom's first memory of being sexually abused by her father at age three.

Sometime around 1965, my mom, Esperanza, and Tío Samuel, dressed up for sibling photos. Tío Samuel's urge to protect my mom started young.

APR · 67

My mom, Esperanza, age 5, all dolled up as the flower girl for her uncle's wedding.

Left to right: Tío Leo, Tío Samuel, my mom, Esperanza, Tío Fernando, and Tío Daniel (bottom) at a time of true sibling unity.

My mom's, Esperanza's, Kindergarten portrait. This was her first experience being immersed in the English language.

Camping with her family was a sacred activity for my mom growing up, where her father could not hurt her. Here she is with her brothers.

My mom, Esperanza, with her mom and brothers during her grade school days. She enjoyed her mom's daily handmade tortillas during this time.

"The Mexican Jackson Five." This is one of my mom's favorite photos of her and her brothers, taken at their home in the early 70s.

This was my mom's, Esperanza's, quinceañera and one of the happiest days of her young life, evident by the beaming smile on her face.

On one of their many desert vacations, my mom, Esperanza, playing around with her brother and best friend Tío Samuel.

Being in nature always brought my mom peace. Here she is as a teenager relaxing on a family trip to the desert.

This is the inspiration for the front cover. My mom, in her mid-teens, posing with a friend's father on his horse in front of Abuelita Elena's home in Purepero, where she always felt safe.

This is one of my favorites: my mom posing for her high school senior picture. She loved school and gladly became heavily involved in student government, sports, and clubs.

Clockwise from bottom left: Tío Leo, Tío Fernando, my mom, Esperanza, Tío Samuel, Tío Daniel in their Huntington Beach home.

You can see why my mom won "best dressed" in college. Here she is at her brother's, Tío Fernando's wedding.

My mom, Esperanza and Abuelita Elena having a blast on a dune buggy on a family trip to the desert.

My mom and dad on their wedding day. It was one of the hottest days of the year, but my mom didn't even notice, she was so happy. Both of their styles are on full display. Notice my dad's white cane. My mom talked him out of wearing a matching top hat.

My parents on their honeymoon in Yosemite, finally on their own together for the first time.

My sister and I, matching as usual in our younger years.

My mom, Esperanza, holding my brother, Ricky, as an infant. My parents were thrilled to have a little boy and my sister and I were enamored with him from the moment we met him.

Me (in the middle) and my sister (to the left) with our cousins and Abuelita Isabella (paternal grandmother) dressed for Our Lady of Guadalupe in my grandparents' home in Purepero.

My parents loved getting us all dressed up for family portraits. Here's our first one as a family of five.

My brother and I on a camping trip. My parents turned their favorite family pastime into one of ours. On this trip we borrowed my abuelitos RV.

My immediate family surrounding our matriarch, Abuelita Elena, on Christmas Eve. Known as the posada in many Latin cultures, this is a big celebration.

My sister Valentina and I performing a Mexican folk dance at a school talent show. We took classes from a well-known group called Ballet Folklorico De Mexico De Amalia Hernandez.

My dad and tíos gathered after one of Tío Samuel's boxing matches in the early 90s. From left to right: Tío Fernando, Tío Daniel, Tío Samuel, Tío Leo, Ricardo (my dad).

Tío Samuel became a professional boxer in his early 20s. His only loss was in Germany against Henry Maske.

The fateful Garfield Journal, where my mother first wrote about her experiences.

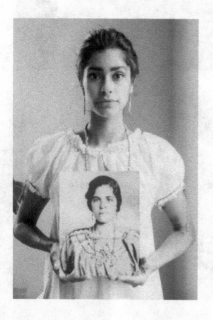

Me, Amelia Rodriguez, in 2018, holding Abuelita Elena's portrait.

17

One Monday evening in 2018, I sought Tío Leo's perspective on that first confrontation with my mom and his parents. Sitting in his living room, engulfed in both our nerves and positivity, a hefty sound system played the song "How to Save a Life" by The Fray softly in the background. I had heard it a million times before, but on this day the lyrics took on new meaning:

Step one, you say we need to talk
He walks, you say sit down, it's just a talk
He smiles politely back at you
You stare politely right on through...
As he begins to raise his voice
You lower yours and grant him one last choice
Drive until you lose the road
Or break with the ones you've followed
He will do one of two things
He will admit to everything
Or he'll say he's just not the same
And you'll begin to wonder why you came

I imagined these lyrics as a reflection for the way Tío Leo must have felt the day he confronted his father in the garage.

Tío Leo let out a heavy sigh, fear of revisiting painful memories etched on his face. I felt the special significance of him agreeing to talk about this for the first time as he slowly opened up to me.

"I was there as support. I do not remember saying anything to either of my parents. It was your mom's time to speak. She wanted a voice and she wanted to make sure she was heard. My heart went out to my sis, and a lot of anger went towards my father — and my mother, to be honest, because she knew and did nothing about it. I was there for my sis though. I was not letting my emotions get in the way of what she wanted to do. That meant fighting the urge to hurt my dad, which I definitely wanted to do."

When my parents finally cut Abuelito Hector and Abuelita Carmen out of our lives, they explained to my siblings and me that Abuelito Hector was a bad man, and we were no longer allowed to see him. My mom found some peace in severing the rotting roots of her life, yet there were times, like in sleep, when she could not escape the terror of her father. She read with resilience and strength her journal entry from September 5th, 1993, 3:20 am.

"I just woke up from a terrible nightmare. In this horrible dream I was lying asleep on the left side of the bed and something was on the right side. I felt somebody walk to my side of the bed and I opened my eyes. It was my father. During this dream my father was living in my home. He told me he did not want to wake Valentina up, so he came to tell me he needed money withdrawn from the bank, ninety two dollars and ninety one cents. I was mixed up and during this confusion he started grabbing my breasts. I kept trying to push his arms back but I couldn't. He was stronger than me. I tried screaming but no sound would come out. At that moment I woke up and I was holding my comforter so tight below my neck to not let anything in or near me. Once I realized I was safe, I released my grip and my fingers were in pain."

My mom redirected her gaze at me. "When you, Valentina, and Ricky were little, I would often wake up terrified. I had many nightmares of my dad trying to molest me and touch you three. There were many nights I dreamt he was trying to kill me and I was running, trying to get away. After the second emergency meeting, it was really hard getting through the weight of it all and I needed more female support. It was clear my brothers were having a difficult time sharing this information with their wives, so I decided I would tell them myself. They were mothers as well, and they needed to know the truth."

She shared the news with each of her sisters-in-law separately. Tía Emma was appalled, learning about abuelito Hector's evil for the first time. Tía Gloria, already in the know, learned more. Horrified as they were, Tía Emma and Tía Gloria were glad to know what kind of man their father-in-law was. The conversations they had with my mother were short and to-the-point, and hardly memorable. Tía Jessica, on the other hand, remembers every detail from hers.

Listening to Tía Jessica, Tío Samuel's wife, describe the events leading up to my mom's reveal was thrilling. We settled on her bed, drinking water with lime ice cubes, a Mexican favorite, as she began to share with unabashed transparency.

"From day one, I never wanted Hector or Carmen holding either of my kids — and this was before I knew anything. I guess you could say it was a gut instinct, but I really had no clue."

I remembered Tía Emma, Tío Leo's wife, saying she felt similarly. Hearing about nature's alarm system in the women of our family, was empowering. We really can rely on our gut as a warning call to protect ourselves and others. It's just a matter of listening to it.

I asked if she remembered the first emergency meeting back in 1990, and her eyebrows immediately shot up, her eyes widening. "Yes! It was super top secret! None of the wives got to know. All I knew was something really big and critical was happening. It was a couple years before I found out the truth. I felt isolated, lied to, and kept in the dark.

"Samuel was crying almost every night at that point, but he would not tell me why. This went on for some time. He became dark and sad, having secret sibling meetings, that I couldn't really ask him about. It was hard for us to have any kind of real exchange about what was going on. I didn't think he was having an affair because he was meeting with his siblings, but he came home broken, and I had no idea why."

The sadness in her voice told of the ache of isolation she felt during this time.

"I eventually stopped asking questions," she recalled. "It felt like if you were not born a Madero, you were out, and you would never feel quite equal. Your grandparents led that attitude in the family. Once Samuel's world crumbled around him, he saw who was really healthy for him. He realized his parents did not walk on water. Your grandparents were awful people, but they made all these great children. Sure, they messed them up a bit, but their children are remarkable people. Samuel was not happy. Who could be? The level of secrecy in the family — it was too much to bear!"

Tía Jessica spoke firmly, yet empathetically, "Samuel never told me what was going on. It was your mom who came over several months after the second emergency meeting happened and started letting me in on the truth.

"She told me, 'The boys are not doing much about what I've shared with them. I know they're in shock and just now starting to grasp the truth. But I cannot watch over and protect all our babies from my father by myself anymore.'

"I was completely confused!" Tía Jessica said to me, looking back on the still coded messaging coming from the Madero clan. "She thought Samuel shared more with me than he actually did, but I still didn't know what the hell was going on. When she realized, she told me everything. We were sitting on my bed, just the two of us — kind of like we are now — and she shared everything she could think of: her own life, what she saw and knew about others, everything! I was in absolute shock."

Hearing again of my mom taking charge, overcoming her fears, and speaking her truth with the women in her life made me proud. As a mother herself, she knew the other mothers in the family needed to know in order to keep everyone as safe as possible. But it was not easy or void of pain, especially after a lifetime of being muffled and suppressed. Finally, she was breaking her silence.

Tía Jessica went on. "I was sick thinking about this poor little girl. From the day she was born, her father was against her. It was hard to hear! I was angry at Samuel for knowing as long as he did and not telling me. He was blinded by loyalty to his family. Your mom let me ask any questions I wanted and answered every one of them. She was done keeping everybody's secrets. She shared her life's story with me as if she were talking about somebody else. She was so used to it, depicting the abuse like it was a part of her everyday life, because it was. The trauma, the drama, it was overwhelming, and she was handling it like a queen. I wanted to honor her, so I tried to take her lead."

I smiled, knowing exactly what she meant and how she felt about the way my mom has always carried herself. She leads her life with love, all the while overcoming deep affliction and anger. At times, as her children, we would experience the wrath of her anger, but we grew up to understand where it came from.

"Samuel was upset at your mom for telling me," Tía Jessica said chuckling and shaking her head slightly. "He thought it was not his sister's place to disclose this to his wife, but he was wrong. First of all, it is her story to tell — not anybody else's — and she has the right to tell whoever she wants. Secondly, it was absolutely the best and right thing to do. And now that I knew, I wondered *Do I have to keep this a secret, too?*
"No! It was not a secret anymore. Some people may have wanted it to be, but the secret was out, and it needed to stay out. Yet, everything from then on, anything that could trigger Samuel and his emotions, I needed to handle with care, because he was broken. At times it seemed he was still enamored with his parents. The mirror was not shattered yet, but it was cracking slowly. It took a while for him to process what he learned about his sister, his brother, his father, and his mother. It would for anyone. I did what I could to support him."

I let out a big sigh, contemplating Tío Samuel's reaction to his wife knowing the truth. I was disappointed by his insistence on secrecy, while simultaneously understanding his need to live in two separate worlds.

Tía Jessica's eyes softened as she spoke about Tío Samuel, "Even though Samuel and I never talked about it in detail, he cried every single night. We would drink our nightly tequila sunrise, make popcorn and once I knew, he would get all teary eyed, lay his head on my lap saying stuff like, 'I never knew,' 'I can't believe my parents are like this,' 'How could we not know?' 'Why didn't Esperanza tell me?'
"What he struggled with most was the fact that he could not protect his sister. Esperanza was his best friend. The two shared a close bond and yet he never knew what she went through. It was this guilt of being almost a twin with her but unable to save her from the monster he called Dad. That ate him up inside."

I groaned with sorrow. My heart broke for Tío Samuel and my other tíos. All he wanted was for everything to be okay, to have a normal life with his parents and have the memories of his childhood not be tarnished forever. It was too late, though. Tío Samuel's happy memories slowly turned to dark clouds, as he tried clutching onto them before they were gone — chasing vanishing fog, he was left standing on the road alone.

There was nothing 'normal' about his parents, and as I let out another heavy sigh, I tried to imagine the internal chaos of realizing your father is one of the worst, most evil men you could fathom. What does that do to a person? Does it break you? Does it harden you? Does it soften you? Does it make you live life with more gratitude? What does it do to your existence? What does it do to your soul?

Throughout this whole process, interviewing each member of my family to explore long buried secrets, I was there to help them let go. To give them a platform to release themselves from burden. Holding onto heavy secrets — consciously or subconsciously — takes a grueling toll on your well-being. It starts in the mind and gradually pervades the body, manifesting in physical discomfort and mental strain, until it has consumed every corner of your life. The guilt, fear, and sadness my tíos battled blurred their senses of self, plunging them into the grey nuance of trauma.

As society begins to reckon sexual abuse and its prevalence, slowly pushing it out from the shadows, we find ourselves wondering what we would do in that situation as a caretaker or victim. In the case of molestation, many believe passionately that they would speak up to save that child or themselves. But the reality of trauma is never as clear-cut as you would expect, especially if you know the predator, which according to RAINN, the Rape, Abuse and Incest National Network, 80% of sexual assault victims do.

Instead, it is a confusing mix of fear, shame, guilt, and paralysis, clouding one's ability to protect even a child, let alone oneself. Therefore, there is no place for judgment in these situations. Unless you have survived horrors like my family has, you will never truly know how you would react to abuse and dehumanization. My hope is that you never have to find out, but if you do, I hope you prove yourself right — that you *would* speak up.

Only Abuelito Hector and Abuelita Carmen are to blame in this scenario. They were the ones who chose to live a life of exploitation, intimidation, and concealment. I place no guilt on my tíos for asking my mom not to press charges, nor on my mom and dad for Valentina's abuse. They were all innocent pawns in the evil game my abuelitos made out of life.

18

One bright, California-perfect day in the spring of 2018, my parents and I pulled up to a beautiful park down by the beach. It was vibrantly green and peacefully quiet, and my mom let us in on her little secret: This was her 'safe space.'

It was a healthy secret, one that gave her a special place all her own, where she would come when she wanted to get away and felt like she was losing it. She wouldn't even leave her car most of the time — just recline her seat, open a door, stare out at nature, and cry. We immediately understood why she made this her safe space. Under a row of slender palm trees reaching high into the sky, I asked my parents to describe the fallout of my sister's assault.

"Well, after confronting my parents with Leo, our family — as in your dad and I, and you three kids — stopped talking to my father and stopped attending family functions. We used to go to every family event, so people started asking questions. This went on for several months until one day your dad ran into my father and Tío Joel at Thrifty's," my mom began.

"No one spent more time with my father than Tío Joel. The two were like brothers, even though Tío Joel was my mom's brother, not your abuelito's. But they knew each other since they were kids."

I curiously turned to my dad, "So...what happened at Thrifty's?"

The memory of December, 1993 returned as he pulled the order of events out of the buried past. "Tío Joel lived close by and your abuelito Hector and him were always together, but even more so now since your abuelito's dark secrets were coming out. He could feel a shift happening and he wanted to control what Tío Joel heard and believed.

"I was walking through the parking lot of Thrifty's, and your abuelito Hector and Tío Joel happened to be walking through at the same time, and we ran into each other at the entrance. I ignored your abuelito, but said hi to Tío Joel, who looked at me with shameful eyes while shaking his head.

"I thought, *Wow, he's wrapped up in Hector's lies*, but I didn't pay much attention and kept it moving. According to Tío Joel, your abuelito turned to him after I walked past and said, 'See? Ricardo doesn't like me. I told you he's mad at me for no good reason.'

"At the time, Tío Joel believed and sided with your abuelito. He was still oblivious to the havoc his brother-in-law and best friend had reaped on the family — his family! I grabbed what I needed in the store and went to checkout. Then, Tío Joel reappeared and gave me another dirty look. To this day, I can still see in my mind, Tío Joel looking at me with that scornful stare. There was no doubt he and your abuelito shared a strong bond. That day, right after our run-in, a horrible lie started spreading about your mom and I."

I was at the height of my investigation into my family's past, and I needed to hear from Tío Joel. Besides Abuelita Carmen, he was the one closest to Abuelito Hector. In a race to gather as much information as I could, we gathered in Tío Joel's dining room, together with my mom and Tía Victoria, his wife. His fair freckled skin brought out his brown eyes and red hair. As he shared more about that day, he looked down at his hands and then back up at me with unease.

Joel and Hector took their Thrifty's beers back to Joel's house, and settled into the backyard game room to drink and shake off the tense interaction they just escaped. It was then that Hector spun the ugly lie about his daughter and son-in-law.

"It's better Carmen and I retire from Huntington Beach. We are going to sell the house and go far away. Esperanza and Ricardo are accusing me of a horrible act that I did not commit."

"No!" Joel protested, instinctively taking his friend's side. "If you want, I will confront Esperanza. It is not right that they're doing this to you. I will talk to them both."

"No, please don't say anything to them," begged Hector.

"How can I not? I'm going to..." Joel started to say.

"No, no. Thank you," interrupted Hector manipulatively, "but don't say anything to them. It's better if we just leave this place so Esperanza and Ricardo can be at peace."

"What is it that they're accusing you of? I don't get it!" exclaimed Joel, desperate to know what was going on.

Tío Joel was too embarrassed to share the details with me about the lie Abuelito Hector told him, so while all together in his dining room, my mom took over. She looked at me with a grin of absurdity and raised eyebrows.

"My father told Tío Joel that when your dad and I were dating, he caught us having oral sex in the living room, with my family in the house. He said he looked through his bedroom window — which faced into the family room — saw your dad down there performing oral sex on me and kicked him out. According to my father, your dad and I were still mad at him for this and we wanted revenge, so he spun the lie that we were retaliating by making up that he molested Valentina.

"Like I told you before, I didn't even kiss your dad until after we were married. He fabricated the whole story and spread it around as the reason we would no longer speak to him or attend family gatherings."

Tío Joel's face was as red as his hair from embarrassment. With a bug-eyed stare, he nodded his head confirming my mother's story.

The fact that her father could so easily put her in this inappropriate and vulnerable position within their own family was further proof to my mom that he truly did not care about her. He did not have the capacity to care. She took the first step in letting him go, surrendering to the truth of his character by finally cutting ties with him, and this nasty, sloppy lie is what he left her with.

During this time, Joel and Victoria were furious with Esperanza and Ricardo and could not believe they would make up such ghastly "lies" about Hector. Deeply entrenched in life with Hector, Joel and Victoria could not yet see past his web of deception. They were entangled, comfortably in the center of the web, going so far as to let others in the family know they were disowning Esperanza.

But as my old friend The Buddha once alluded, *Three things cannot be long hidden: The sun, the moon, and the truth.*

Her tío and tía were more like parents to her than her own, and they were slipping away. Devastated and exhausted, Esperanza was reaching a new low.

Esperanza had been losing her sanity for a while now, often leaving the kids with Ricardo to go to the park where she could run, scream, and cry into the boundless sky. At times, Valentina, Amelia and Ricky, now nine, seven, and four years old, would find their mother with a far-removed look in her eyes, spaced out, unaware of their presence. Other times, she could be found kneeling down on the bathroom floor scrubbing the same spot, over and over again. At one point, she found herself curled up in the fetal position in the shower, sobbing, the water unable to wash away her pain.

Her tears merged with the falling water, and while on her side hugging her knees, she realized she was having a mental breakdown — and she could not afford to lose control. In a swift instant, she stopped crying and sat up. Quickly shaking her head side to side, she let out deep breaths. She had three kids and a husband. She could not let the density of her burdens get the best of her. She needed to crawl out of the darkness and let in the light, fearing she could be institutionalized if she didn't — but she wasn't quite ready.

She was still consumed with guilt and trapped in a world of lies. During this time, her brother Samuel would go to her house often to check on her. He knew what to look for: an empty fridge and a dirty house. Esperanza was known to have a stocked kitchen and spotless home, always prepared to nourish and host her family and friends. So if it wasn't, he knew she was not doing well.

Samuel was always there for her in the bleakest of times, one of the main people in her life as consistent a force as her faith in God. In these most trying times, she continued to recite her favorite scripture: *"For I reckon that the sufferings of this present time are not worthy to be compared with the glory which shall be revealed in us."* -Romans 8:18

Spiraling further into a deep depression, dark thoughts swarming her mind, Esperanza decided to call on her support system. Her closest female cousins and friends. Despite spending her childhood with these women, she never turned to them about the abuse she endured. Now was the time. She waited long enough, and the guilt of her own daughter's abuse was eating her alive — if she stayed silent, she feared the police could take all her children away if they found out Valentina was sexually abused.

Esperanza phoned her cousin Jasmine to let her know she was not doing well and needed to gather the women in their life at the park as soon as possible. She did not say much more than that, but Jasmine took the call seriously, knowing her cousin's tone well. She wasted no time, called on their network, and the next day they women gathered.

It was April 14th, 1994, midday, and one by one, the women arrived: Jasmine, Elsa, Erica, Sara, and others, all there to support Esperanza. It seemed they had the park to themselves, and after affectionate greetings and friendly small talk, the women settled in a circle on the grass. Esperanza initiated the conversation, and in delicate stillness, they listened.

The women knew Esperanza wanted to discuss something severe, but could only speculate until she began revealing the truth of her horrific childhood, who her father really was, and what he had done to Valentina.

The women's blood collectively boiled as memories from each woman's past thrust to the fore. The women stared at Esperanza, paralyzed, listening. Finally, the sisters sat together confronting decades of their own suppression, guilt in their guts. Slowly, one by one, the women broke their silence.

"Me too."

"Me too."

"Me too."

"Me too."

"Me too."

It turned out Esperanza was not the only childhood victim of Hector Madero, nor the only one keeping a devastating secret of sexual trauma. None of the women shared their stories with one another before this period. Instead, the women let the pain fester and infect their lives, feeling alone in their silence for far too long.

Learning more about her cousins' and friends' experiences with her father, Esperanza shriveled back into herself. Her secret revealed a bigger mess than she could ever have imagined.

Esperanza never considered the possibility of her father abusing anyone else except for the instances she knew — the childhood cousins and friends who never slept over again. Her brain went to dark places, but never here. She gasped with grief and shock, "Oh my gosh. I had no idea!"

The women shared their stories, and the injustices lingered thick.

"He made me touch his penis."

"He would kiss me."

"When I would spend the night, he would sneak into where I slept and put his hands down my underwear."

"He would lie on top of me and hump me."

"There was penetration."

"The little that I remember is more than enough. I don't want to know more."

"Why did we not talk about this when we were younger?!"

"I wish we would have."

The more the women released the rot from within, the more the thickness around them thinned. The discussion returned to Valentina, and their maternal strength roared out.

"This has to stop! We have to stop him! What if he continues with Valentina, or gets to Amelia or any of his granddaughters next!" they volleyed with concern.

"Enough is enough! We must intervene."

The conversation concluded with a call to action, as the women embraced one another in shared affliction and strength. Airing these dark and long-kept secrets was refreshing for them all, but did not relieve Esperanza's immense struggle. She spiraled further. The shock, guilt, and shame of how many people her father molested was reaching a breaking point. She left the park quickly and drove home, while many of the other women stuck around, basking in the relief of not being alone.

The sunlight and trees cradled them in the serenity of the park as the women huddled next to their cars, strategizing. Given how much trouble Esperanza was having with this volatile discovery, the women agreed on a collective ruling: They would report Hector Madero to the police department — and not tell Esperanza until after it was done. Knowing Esperanza was the one most affected by this monster, it was their way of protecting her. Getting him thrown into prison was the only way to be sure he would never harm a child again, and they knew Esperanza was in no place to handle the weight of this effort.

The gathering at the park awakened the little girl inside each of them with the determination to end decades of fear, torture, and abuse. Empowered by their unity, the women decided to tell their parents the truth about their "beloved" Hector, what happened to them as children, and what was happening again to the next generation. They were steadfast in breaking this vicious cycle, ripping the diseased roots from their grips.

The women could no longer bear the shame, guilt, and worry they had been harboring all these years.

Not long after arriving home, Esperanza received a call from one of the women in the circle, her cousin Elsa. Elsa was the daughter of Tío Joel and Tía Victoria. She asked Esperanza to come to her house to be with her and her sister, Sara, while they told their parents about the sexual abuse they endured as children.

Esperanza hung up the phone, got in her car, and headed over. The meeting in the park — the power she felt being validated and supported — was the momentum she needed to actualize her vision and pull herself out of the dark. This time, there was no going back. The news spread like wildfire, as the webs of deception were finally tearing apart.

Inside Joel and Victoria's car, nervous tension was building. They could not imagine what emergency Elsa and Sara wanted to speak to them about.

En route to Elsa's, they received a call from Miranda, Joel and Carmen's sister. She spoke frantically, making little sense, sounding manic and a bit insane. Concerned and confused, Joel and Victoria decided to check in on Miranda on their way to Elsa's. There was a powerful force circulating and it was impacting more than just their daughters.

The couple arrived at Miranda's to find her crying, her daughter Jasmine and close family friend Susana seated next to her. Although Susana did not join the women at the park, she gathered to speak with Jasmine's mother. Jasmine and Susana had just shared with Miranda their experiences of abuse at the hands of Hector.

Miranda cried in a state of shock. Stunned themselves, Joel and Victoria jumped back in their car and drove hurriedly to their daughters with a good guess of what to expect. Elsa and Sara, and to their surprise, Esperanza, were situated in the kitchen, anxiously awaiting their arrival.

Joel and Victoria shook with fear as they listened to Elsa and Esperanza lead the dreaded, but critical conversation. Joel lost it, weeping and begging Esperanza and his daughters to forgive him for being so blind. His heart shattered for his daughters, for his niece, and for his friendship with Hector. He could not take knowing his children were molested by his best friend, his role model. He felt he failed in protecting his own children, his niece included.

A feverish hurricane stormed through him and Victoria, as the three women struggled to see their elders so tortured by the news. The shared misery of everyone in the room was palpable. Even though Elsa, Sara, and

Esperanza did nothing wrong, they could not shake a heavy sense of humiliation divulging this intimate, twisted darkness to their parents.

Joel and Victoria's whole world came to a sudden crawl. This was one of their closest friends, their family, brother-in-law, and confidant. How could this have happened under their care? How could someone so horrific hide in plain sight, masquerading as the respected leader of the family? They were in complete disbelief, but the truth was beginning to sink in. Hector was a fraud, a liar, and a criminal. Carmen's inability and refusal to fight for her own children, and theirs, was real. That day, and its cascade of revelations, felt at once like an eternity and a sudden death — the death of life as they knew it.

On their drive home, Victoria grew solemn and introspective, while Joel was overcome with madness, one thought on his mind, *Kill him!* When they arrived home, Victoria quickly followed Joel into the house trying to convince him not to go over to Hector's.

"Think about your family!" she said loudly, with an equal dose of earnestness and love.

Tío Joel retorted, "I want to smash his face in!" He walked straight through the house, grabbed a bat, and jumped back into the car. Victoria stood in the doorway of their home and stared at him, fearful that there was no stopping Joel in his fury. Adrenaline rushed through his body, his heart rate and blood pressure soared, and his pupils contracted. He was choosing fight over flight, as if it were his life or Hector's, and he was not going to let Hector's evil win. The monster needed to be eliminated. Joel turned on the car and sat in the driver's seat with the bat in between his legs, screaming to himself, "I'm going to smash your head in, Hector! I'm going to kill you!"

Saying the words out loud forced him to realize what he was contemplating. Victoria's voice echoed in his mind as he talked himself off the ledge.

"Think about your family. You are going to kill him, and then what? The police are going to throw you in prison and lock you up for the rest of your life. You can *not* do that to your family," Joel pleaded with himself, quelling the fire burning through his body.

The ease with which his urge to kill Hector erupted scared him, as it did Ricardo. Joel looked at Victoria standing in the doorway, panicked and sad. He took a deep breath, got out of the car, and walked back up towards his wife, tears in both of their eyes. She exhaled with relief and smiled sadly at him as he walked through the door with a change of heart, embracing him and rubbing his back as he returned into their home.

Finally, the family was shown the light, thanks to the bravery of these women. With a forcefield of strength around them, the band of sisters kept on marching towards their goal of justice. After that fateful afternoon in the park, and talking to their parents, the women busied themselves calling other cousins and Esperanza's childhood friends whom they suspected may have been molested and giving them the option to join them in their march to the police department the following day.

Many of the women decided to go, while others had personal reasons for declining. Some thought the "little" that happened to them as children was not worthy of a police report.

Individuals abused go through many loops of conversations in their heads, often convincing themselves the trauma they experienced was "not that bad." But when an adult, decades older than you, touches you inappropriately as a child — even once — that is a crime, and justice should be served. When we shift the shame from the victim to the predator, we flourish.

19

The band of sisters settled on 10 a.m. to meet at the police station. Eager and fearful, the women filed into the parking lot. By this time, the group had expanded beyond just the women at the park. Friends, cousins, and sisters gathered and marched into the station, immediately telling the officers at the front desk why they were there. Shocked, the officers asked them to be seated in the lobby and wait while they called them in, one by one, to speak to the detective. The second hand on the station's wall clock sounded loudly as each woman waited her turn to speak her truth.

After sharing their darkest and longest kept secrets to the police and detective, the women walked out of the station and regrouped. Some were quiet, some were crying, while others showed unflinching anger. A heavy sense of disappointment fell over them like a ceiling of thick smoke.

The women were told by the detective that because of the statute of limitations, there was almost nothing they could do, other than go to Hector's home and question him to see if there was current information to open up an investigation. The only solid hope was Valentina, since the abuse she endured was within the statute of limitations. She was the only one who could get him thrown in prison. A ten-year-old child, testifying against her abuelito, describing her sexual abuse in detail. It was almost unthinkable, and sure to retraumatize her.

Although the knowledge of this horrific man was finally out in the open, he was still free to roam about and inflict more harm. The women were disgusted at the thought. They felt defeated, having finally mustered the courage to report their assailant, only to learn it was "too late" by legal standards. But they were lucky — most women in their position feel defeated to learn that reporting their assault entails being shamed by cops and others in their community. But these detectives seemed to take their case seriously and were determined to help. Their first step was to contact Esperanza, the person most affected.

Learning that the primary impediment to bringing justice to these scarred women, and preventing this predator from abusing more children, was a statute of limitations, was disheartening — it meant no justice. How do you put a statute of limitations on child sexual abuse, one of the most heinous crimes a person can commit? Especially when you consider how disincentivized individuals are to come forward, and the time it takes to find the courage to finally do so. This keeps perpetrators free, survivors imprisoned in their own trauma, and more potential victims vulnerable. It is a fatal flaw of the justice system, and my family was a casualty of its influence.

A wildfire was burning all around Hector and Carmen, but they had yet to inhale the smoke, unaware of how much truth was awakened and in motion. Esperanza was quite literally going insane and it was a feat it hadn't happened sooner.

"Hello?" she answered the phone.
"Hi, Esperanza, it's Susana. We have a conversation long overdue."
Esperanza, tethered to the wall by the corded phone, knew exactly what she was referring to. She pictured her father laying on top of 10-year-old Susana, while she lay next to her, back turned. She felt the wind knocked out of her, grabbed onto a stool to hold herself up, and replied: "Yes, we do."
"Do you remember when I stayed the night at your house, and we woke up the next day and my panties were down?" Susana asked. "Well, I was awake."

Susana went on to describe how she pretended not to know what happened by faking to be asleep, when in reality, she was awake the whole time. She went home and told a trusted adult, who told her to be quiet out of fear. She told Esperanza she thought it ended with them, but after hearing the news about the park gathering, realized it did not. Susana, who had officially joined the march of women, informed Esperanza that the women went to the police department to report her father earlier that day, and that the detective would be getting in touch with her next.

Esperanza hung up the phone and dropped her head. Her almond-shaped eyes stared at the floor as she gripped the edge of the stool tighter to keep from crumbling to the ground. Before she could regain her balance, she received another call, this time from a Huntington Beach detective.

Esperanza collected herself, scared into submission by her own courage, the detective's authority, and the gravity of the situation. The two began discussing Esperanza's options and concluded their conversation by agreeing that she would go to the Huntington Beach Police Station at her earliest convenience. She busied herself nervously, roaming the house picking toys up, folding blankets, and cleaning dishes, before laying on the grass in the backyard to watch her children play.

Finally, at 32, the courage and strength to detach from her Stockholm Syndrome — a confused and yet self-protecting response of revere for and obedience to one's abuser — galvanized her. But even though she cut her father out of her life, he was still her father, and going to the police department was not easy.

Ousting her father to the law was the right thing to do, and she knew it. With her support system of women and husband by her side, the truth was seeping out. She had to lead the fight. It was her time. She was a mother now and was devoted to living openly in her truth and protecting her children — an instinct that came naturally to her, despite her mother's failure to harness it. There was no shortage of women behind her, willing to take a stand against her father. Still, there were four other people she needed to consider: her brothers. She needed to tell them her plan.

She called Fernando, the oldest, and told him everything — the park gathering, their tías and tíos finding out, their cousins going to the police, an investigation being opened, and finally an impending meeting with the detectives — and asked him to relay this message to their brothers.

Shortly after, that same day, another phone call was made just down the street. It was Carmen phoning her brother Joel. She became aware of the accusations filed against Hector — although it was never confirmed how — and she hoped to reason with her brother whom she was close to.

"Hi, Joel," she said in an anxious tone. "I just heard about the accusations. Can you please ask your daughters to rescind them? Please! I *promise* we will leave this place. You will never have to deal with us again!"

"No! No, Carmen," Joel expressed himself strictly. "I will not do that. They are my daughters. I cannot do that. I am very sorry, but no."

"Please, let's talk about this. I know the girls will listen to you!" she pleaded hopelessly. "I know they will if you just talk to them. Joel, please!"

"You're right. They may just do it if I ask them to. That is how selfless my daughters are. But I cannot do that. I won't. I am leaving what you and Hector did up to the law and to God."

Carmen cried, begging her brother to change his mind, but he would not.

"I wish you well sister," he told her sadly and hung up.

That was the last time the sister and brother would speak for decades.

Esperanza took the day to process. By the end of it, she was reassured in her decision to go to the police station the next day. Her brothers may not have been ready, but she knew this was vital, not only for her and her daughter's emotional freedom, but for all affected by Hector. The next day she marched into the Huntington Beach Police Department by herself. Detective Dan, the detective who called the day before, came right out. He was friendly and led her into a room where they could sit down and talk. She looked down at the recorder he put on the table and shifted in her seat.

"Is it okay if I record our conversation?" he asked.

Taking a deep breath in, Esperanza firmly replied, "Yes." It had taken her over twenty-five years, but she was determined to speak her truth far and wide, no matter the consequences.

Detective Dan turned on the recorder and began his questioning.

Do you consider your dad to be a dangerous person? Why is he dangerous? Can you tell me what happened to you? Have you ever reported your dad in the past? Why have you decided to report him now? Is there anything else you can tell me that would be helpful for this investigation?

Esperanza answered to the best of her ability. He made her feel comfortable; he was a nice person, sympathetic, and seemed genuinely interested in helping her. The two finished their talk, and Detective Dan walked Esperanza out, reassuring her his team would do everything in their power to investigate her father and try to bring justice to her family and friends.

The best option was finding recent incidents of sexual abuse by Hector in the Huntington Beach district. Since the abuse towards Valentina happened outside of Huntington Beach, she was told to go to the Fountain Valley Police Department, the suburb where the abuse took place. They shook hands and Esperanza returned to her car feeling sick yet empowered. She put her seatbelt on and broke down, shedding her blues and finding liberation. She wiped her eyes, took a deep breath, and drove to the Fountain Valley Police Department.

Reporting the abuse against Valentina was the roughest part for Esperanza. If charges were to be pressed, individuals on the case would need to take ten-year-old Valentina to Orangewood Home — the same place Ricky was taken several years prior — to undergo a rape exam.

A friend of Esperanza's, who was an attorney and dealt with such cases, told her the experience of being poked and prodded would be more traumatic for Valentina than if they just left it alone. Valentina might also see it as her mother allowing strangers to touch her. The idea of jeopardizing her daughter's trust again was enough to change Esperanza's mind. She decided not to press charges on Valentina's behalf. The last thing she wanted was to exacerbate her daughter's trauma.

Although Esperanza had decided not to press charges, she knew the detectives were going to question her father and she held hope that somehow they would find evidence to incriminate him. For two days, she nervously awaited any news, knowing that Detective Dan would call after questioning her father. Every time the phone rang, nerves shot through her body. But, nervous as she was, she was ready to hear what the detectives could or could not report. Two days after going to the police she finally got the call. Esperanza picked up anxiously on the first ring.

"Hello?"

"Hello. Is Esperanza home?"

"This is her."

"Hi Esperanza. This is Detective Dan. I have some news. We went to your parents' house to question your father, but he was not there. Nobody was there. We have gone back several times, but we cannot seem to find him. We're wondering if you know where he is?"

Esperanza's body went limp. She could barely hear what Detective Dan was saying. Questions raced through her mind of her father's whereabouts. There was really nowhere else her father would be since he was retired now, and her mother was usually home.

"What do you mean you can't find him?" asked Esperanza in fear.

"We have tried the house several times with no luck. I'm wondering if you can go into your parents' house and look around for anything we could use as hard evidence. Inappropriate pictures of children, journal entries where he may have written about breaking the law, anything."

Disappointed the detectives did not even get the chance to question her father, Esperanza stressed how hard all of this was on her and her family. The news from the detectives could have been a reassuring jolt of energy — if she knew she'd find something — but she was scared and did not feel sane enough to sneak around her parents' home. She hoped there was another way, but hung up the phone disheartened. She promised herself, her cousins, and the detective that she would be a main witness if those wishing to bring charges were able to bring him to court, adamant to help in any way she could. But Hector's disappearance was beyond her control. The chance to bring legal justice to the family was fading. In her deflated state, her mind went blank and she began to cry.

🕊

Feeling deflated myself, I asked her what happened after that call.

"I never asked my brothers if they knew where he was. I knew whatever they shared with me I would need to disclose to the detectives right away, and I was not comfortable putting my brothers in that situation. I wanted my dad to be investigated, but I wanted to keep a balance with my brothers, who were still reeling from this explosion. I was unstable and unwell — I was not in the state of mind to actively participate in an investigation into my own father. I just wanted him locked up."

Within days of my mom receiving the news that her father disappeared, she and my dad received a call from a cousin in Purepero. Recently alerted to the family drama, she informed them that Abuelito Hector and Abuelita Carmen arrived days earlier to take refuge…they fled the country. Evidently, Abuelito Hector told people he and Abuelita Carmen were moving to Purepero to care for his mother, Abuelita Elena, because she was getting older. My parents were grateful for the call; the search was complete. Abuelito Hector was located.

Days later, it was discovered that Abuelito Hector and Abuelita Carmen went into hiding the night before the detectives went to their home. They fled to a distant tía's house in California, Tía Delfina, who knew nothing about what was going on. I'm certain my abuelitos lied about why they were there, and after a couple days of asylum, they fled to Mexico. They packed only a couple suitcases, leaving the majority of their belongings behind, as if they would be back any day. Shortly thereafter, Hector and Carmen hired movers to pack and ship what was left in California, to Mexico.

🕊

Though legal justice would not be served, our families began to find peace in speaking out and having Abuelito Hector and Abuelita Carmen gone. Our community of families, though devastated, were finding solace in the continued strength of our bonds.

The reality of this story and so many like it is that some of the women who were molested as children tried going to adults they trusted. As children they expected these adults to protect them. But due to a combination of culture, religion, intimidation, and fear, these children were told to keep quiet. They saw their trusted adult turn the other way and pretend it never happened.

Molestation is an egregious loss of innocence, stolen from a child by an adult they were told they could trust. Assembling the courage at a young age to tell someone what happened, that someone violated the most private parts of you, is a mountainous task. The shame is matched only by boundless hope that the adult will speak up and protect you. When they do not, it is crushing.

The child then realizes life around them is not the safe haven they thought it was, the gravity of which can lead to isolation, fear, and depression. The crack in the facade is so deep, it drags through them like an anchor of disappointment.

The question then becomes: Will you become the kind of adult children can trust? Will you use your voice when a child's is muffled? Will you break the silence? What will you do?

20

The bad guy got away, vanishing with his incidental partner in crime. And the crumbling of their empire left in its wake the need to re-build. Abuelita Carmen and Abuelito Hector's punishment was a loneliness like they'd never known. Oh, how far the mighty fell.

And with the force of their fall, the dust swirled thick, with no settling in sight. The absence of our fallen matriarch and patriarch was the silver lining in a cruel and crushing reality for everyone. While us kids never fully understood what was going on, we were intuitive — as kids often are — and we could sense the heavy, black cloud lurking over our family. It followed us throughout life, until we processed who our abuelitos really were and the impact of their sins.

I was seven when my abuelitos fled. I felt abandoned, rejected even. I saw my abuelitos every single week of my life up to that point. Their absence left a sudden hole in my world. I longed for Abuelita Carmen's snail shaped pasta soup, and Abuelito Hector's boisterous laugh, before I understood its sinister undertones.

I do not blame my mom or dad for allowing us around Abuelito Hector. It may be hard to rationalize how they did this, but then again, so is it to have your father — or your wife's father — turn out to be a serial pedophile, and your mother his enabler. The mastery and extent of my Abuelito Hector's manipulation was enough to deceive anyone.

To understand and truly grasp my parents' choices, we need to wholly place ourselves in their reality. Even as their daughter, that is a daunting task.

A little girl. Raped by her father since she was three, continuously exploited and controlled throughout her formative years, and brutally beaten. Punished for tales her father twisted to fit his demented narrative, reasoning himself into dark delirium, and thus creating a world of confusion. She looked to her parents for guidance on how to navigate life.

Instead, they made her fight their incessant barbarity to survive, like a hell pulling her down inside her own home.

I place no blame. Not on my mom.

A young man. Slowly learning the tragic upbringing of the love of his life. Born in the small town of Purepero, Mexico, then to Mexico City for a better education, and eventually a grand voyage into the United States by seventeen. He married that love of his and quickly found himself riddled with anger, fear, confusion, and sadness. Without understanding the complexities of trauma, he thought the sexual abuse had stopped. He was following his wife's lead when it came to his father-in-law.

His struggle to emotionally support his wife and himself in those early years of their marriage brought the same weight of shame abuse usually does, despite him never being a victim. Having children would shift his perspective on how to overcome trauma in a healthy way — talking was the first step.

I place no blame. Not on my dad.

Truth be told, I place no blame on any person. Not even Abuelito Hector. I understand that this abuse goes beyond him. There is no use in harboring blame. It brings only resentment and anger that I do not want in my life, that I do not want in my body.

Over dried mangos with chili, my mom untangled more of the web of lies. "I found out my father was telling Abuelita Elena lies about why he fled, which explained why she stopped talking to me for a bit. I was devastated. I needed to get my thoughts together, so I took off on a three-day retreat to help me figure out what to do next.

"At the retreat I spoke to a priest and told him what was going on. He was wise and his counseling helped a lot. He recommended I have no type of relationship with my parents at all. He told me I did not have to ever see or talk to my mother or father again, and I could forgive them without ever having to have any kind of relationship with them. I told him about Abuelita Elena, how she was my best friend growing up, how my parents fled and moved in with her, and were telling her lies. He didn't think I should try talking with her either, but I prayed on it until I found my answer.

"I decided I would go to Mexico and confront my parents in front of Abuelita Elena. I wanted my father to confess in front of his own mother what he did to me and Daniel."

She felt confident about her decision, and while on her retreat, bought Abuelita Elena a green and white statue of the Virgin Mary.

Esperanza came home from her retreat and let her brothers in on her plan. They were nervous, yet supportive, and decided to accompany their sister, satisfying a need they likely each had, too. Esperanza's brothers wanted a confession out of their father as well. Fernando, Samuel, and Leo all decided to join her, while Daniel endured all the torture he could on the matter and decided to stay behind.

Back at Samuel's house, the veil was lifted on the family secrets. Slowly, he began to talk to Jessica about his father. He told her that he would be going to Mexico to get a confession from his parents, and that he would let everybody around him know the truth. Jessica was happy to be witnessing this breakthrough and was tremendously supportive. Samuel also told her that he was going to offer his mom the opportunity to come home and have a life with her kids and grandkids, but that it was take-it-or-leave-it deal.

Jessica placed her hand on Samuel's back and told him Carmen could absolutely live with them. Samuel sniffled repeatedly and smiled at Jessica with deep gratitude.

The group of siblings arrived in Purepero and went straight to Abuelita Elena's house. Esperanza immediately gave her a hug, but quickly realized it was not being reciprocated. Instead, her abuelita was cold and standoffish. Esperanza was baffled and letting her imagination run wild with the outrageous lies her father must have told her to make her act this way. She could not wait another minute to address the elephant in the room.

"Okay. We're here! We came to talk, so let's talk," expressed Esperanza. All seven of them — the four siblings, their parents, and Abuelita Elena — made their way to the bedroom where Hector and Carmen were staying. On two adjacent beds, the family faced each other, Hector and Carmen on one bed, the brothers, Esperanza, and Abuelita Elena on the other.

Esperanza commenced.

"We're here because we want Abuelita to know the truth."

She went on, shedding what felt like her entire life's story to her own family — a story each of them either concealed or never knew. She made clear that she wanted her father to confess, right there, in front of all of them.

"No, it's not true, it's not true!" Hector proclaimed firmly.

"Abuelita, he sexually molested Valentina, too!" Esperanza howled back.

"Why would you say these things! It's not true!" Hector dug his hole deeper.

"How can you sit there and say it's not true? Abuelita, my mom would send me to the master bedroom with my dad's dinner knowing he was going to molest me!" Esperanza roared.

"You're a liar! It's not true!" Hector echoed furiously.

Carmen felt internally crippled, barely a word out of her mouth, but plenty of tears. Hector sat stern-faced and maintained his position of being falsely accused. Esperanza had enough. She stood up, looked directly at both of her parents and said, "If you don't tell the truth, I am getting up and walking out of here, and you will never see me again."

Almost immediately, as if rehearsed, Fernando, Samuel, and Leo stood up alongside their sister, looked directly at their parents and echoed Esperanza's threats.

Strengthened by their collective power and bond, the four of them waited one beat and walked out of the room, through the courtyard, into the foyer, and towards the front door. Carmen wailed in sadness as Hector broke down screaming and crying and running after them, "Come back! Come back! It's true! It's true! What they're saying is true!"

All concept of time dissolved for the siblings, as they heard their father finally, for the first time ever, admit to all the harm he caused. The four of them erupted crying, and Esperanza felt as if she had collapsed. She had to look down to confirm she was still upright. The siblings' grief clawed at their insides, but they knew what they had to do: turn around, go back inside, and reckon with the truth together.

All seven adults, tearful and anxious, let the words pour out, each expressing their agony and vindication in their own ways. The siblings tried picking up the pieces of themselves that had shattered over the years.

Hector confessed, and Abuelita Elena, a tiny woman, grew to the size of Goliath, colossal wrath steaming out of her body. She was deceived by her own son, whom she always respected and loved, coming to find he was the worst kind of sinner there was, a pedophile, and the most damning kind — one who molested his own kin. She raged at Hector and Carmen.

"Why did you not give her to me?! You could have given her to me! If you did not want her, if you were not going to take care of her, you should have given her to me!"

She directed her stare at Carmen, and yelled, "You are just as guilty as he is! You knew about it and did nothing! You are both guilty!"

That night, Esperanza slept in Abuelita Elena's bed, as she often did on childhood trips to Purepero. She wiped her eyes as Abuelita Elena held her, rubbing her back until she fell asleep. In the morning, Esperanza gave her abuelita the Virgin Mary statue. Abuelita Elena looked at it and started crying.

"What's wrong?" asked Esperanza.

"Now I know you have been sent by God."

"What?" Esperanza asked, a bit confused.

"A few days before you arrived, I was crying because I was told you were coming to Mexico to kill your dad, and I was afraid. I would go to the backyard and cry endlessly, praying to God. One day, while I was in the backyard, the Virgin Mary appeared looking exactly like this statue, dressed in green and white. I know now you were sent by God, mija."

The trip was an emotional upheaval of memories from years of torture, anger, and secrecy. By the end of the short trip, Abuelita Elena and Esperanza had mended their wounds and strengthened their strained relationship. Esperanza was glad she never let go of her abuelita. Confronting her father, and first going on the retreat to prepare, were essential in her rebuilding. Abuelita Elena grew scared of her own son and felt conflicted by the instinctual love for him she could not banish.

From the downstairs of Tío Leo's home, we watched the sun slowly tuck away until it was gone. He looked contemplative.

"My father hightailed right on out of here, and my mom went with him. My dad denied it all the way until he couldn't anymore. We were there to set the story straight, but as with any guilty person, it was *deny, deny, deny.* They could have their hand in the cookie jar and still look right at you and say, 'I'm not stealing cookies.'

"We stood in his face and told him to own up to the truth or lose us all forever. That got to him. Our mom loved us and did not want to lose us, but some of her decisions had already drawn a wedge between us. My dad did not admit what he did for a very long time. I don't know why anybody like him would, because if abusing children is the way you choose to live your life, you are a coward. I would never act so maliciously, affecting somebody for their entire life, and generations to come."

I immediately began to cry, hearing him acknowledge that my abuelito's actions affected my generation as well. These influences seeped into our lives, sometimes with a boom, other times more gradually. I smiled at Tío Leo and exhaled, allowing the heaviness to leave my body.

Cross-legged on her bed, Tía Jessica chimed in about the siblings' return home after that trip.

"I was super thankful Grandma Carmen was not with your uncle Samuel when he got home. I didn't want her in my home. She couldn't take care of her own daughter with love, what was she going to do to mine? When your mom and the boys got back, we kept a tight family unit with all the siblings and kids. We were a family, and even though we felt alone at times, we were all going through this together."

I have always imagined the moment my mom and tíos walked away from their parents as an extraordinary display of empowerment by community, large or small. Whether intentional or not, they empowered each other to keep going and hold out hope for resolve, however subconsciously.

For my mom and tíos — and eventually for us kids — going up against the people who brought them into this world was a soul-reviving step in the right direction. Hearing this story from the people who lived it and understanding the strength it required for them to unite against their fallen heroes has been one of the great inspirations of my life. My mom and her brothers came together and stepped into their somber familial truth, shedding unstoppable light on their shared darkness.

21

Abuelito Hector was not a changed man. Despite his confession and breaking down by the threat of losing his children forever, he was not prepared to reckon with who he was nor was he committed to change. He carried on with his sadistic ways, void of any empathy, unable to grasp the revulsions of his actions, or to even care.

My mom, on the other hand, and against all odds, was born with the empathy of a glorified soul. She and my tíos shared more love and respect than Abuelito Hector could ever dream of redeeming.

Tío Leo thought back on his parents flee. "My dad left because he knew the accusations were true. At that point, we were done defending him, and maybe he felt that. He knew the repercussions of being investigated and likely arrested would be public humiliation and prison time, where he may not make it out alive. Since he was already retired, fleeing to Mexico was an easy choice. He could live like a king there, or risk public humiliation, isolation, and prison time here. For him, leaving meant making it all go away, out of sight out of mind. He left, and my mom went with him."

He looked down at his hands in sadness before looking back up and reconfiguring his straight face. "She chose to leave. It was an extremely poor decision, but that is the person she loved. She loved him even after knowing what he did and who he really was. She is not educated, and he is the only person she was ever with. She was probably more scared of not being with him.

"I am not justifying her actions, I am just trying to understand them. I am sure she was equally as scared, but she must have known her choice would eventually lead to a complete disconnect from her kids." He drifted off in a tone of sorrow, shrugged his shoulders, and let his face turn to a look of indifference.

Under an open blue sky, over fresh mangoes, cashews, and green tea, Tío Joel and Tía Victoria opened up to me, my mom, and my dad in their backyard one afternoon.

"How did you feel after you found out your best friend sexually molested your children and nieces, and your sister did nothing to stop it?" I directed the blunt and straightforward question at Tío Joel.

He looked at me with loving eyes. "How do you think we felt? Bad. We shared a life with them. We trusted them with all our hearts. To then learn what they did — you lose your ability to trust anyone.

"I loved your abuelito very much. I respected him. He was in my life since I was twelve years old when he started dating Carmen. He was like an older brother. I fell into his trap. I did *not* like that he drank a lot. There were times I would try and stop drinking, and he would plead with me, 'Come on, Chon! Just have another drink!' and I would follow his lead. People used to call us 'Los Chones' as a nickname. He was Chano and I was Chon, two Mexican comedians from the 70s."

Tío Joel let his hand, slightly curled into a fist, fall on the table with a thud as his voice became stronger.

"How do you think your abuelitos were doing out there all alone? They lost all of their loved ones." He let out a melancholic exhale. "Soon after your abuelitos fled, someone told me they bought a beautiful home in Mexico, and all I could think was, *'They may have the most beautiful home, but how do they feel inside? How do you think they're doing all by themselves? They're rotting!'* Carmen should have taken him to be treated or gone to the police. Maybe there were doctors who could have helped him, maybe not, but at least he would have been locked up far away from the family, away from the children."

With a lump in his throat, Tío Joel carried on. "He seemed respectable. Why would anyone think he wasn't, let alone that he was somebody else entirely? He had two faces, a good one and a bad one. He was with God and with the devil."

He shook his head in disbelief. "Sometimes I feel it was more Carmen's fault than his, because she covered it up. Hector getting locked up was in my sister's hands, but she did nothing about it. She is also guilty. I never wanted to speak to her again — my own sister. And for decades I didn't."

I was learning how outraged and crushed people were by Abuelita Carmen, as well. It was inconceivable to most of the family that she knew for so long and did nothing about it. Abuelito Hector's capacity for neglect and malevolence was limitless. And so, I made it my life's mission to live in direct opposition of this, to be loving and nurturing. With every uncomfortable conversation, learning the darkest details of my family history, I found myself growing more comfortable in my own skin. Learning to talk openly about sexual abuse with others was undeniably awkward, embarrassing, and certainly harrowing at times. But honoring the truth and breaking our family's silence allowed a flood of relief and strength to take over.

As we ate mangoes, my mom and I talked while my dad, Tío Joel and Tía Victoria attentively listened. "I wish my father would have gone to prison for the rest of his life. Maybe I could have put him there in 1990 if I really pushed it, but my brothers were not ready, and to this day, I understand that."

Not once was she ever mad at them for not supporting pressing charges after that first emergency meeting. I admired my mom and her capacity for love despite her history of neglect. I clutched onto this feeling and her every word.

"Sometimes I feel like I was a coward. I didn't press charges on my own behalf, because I was confused and scared. It was hard for me, as his daughter, to put him in prison. But once he touched Valentina, I did not care. I wanted him gone and behind bars. But then he disappeared. I wish he paid for what he did. It is only fair he would have gone to prison for the crimes he committed, even though he probably would have been killed quickly."

"Would you have been okay with that?" I asked, curiosity holding my eyebrows up.

"With him getting killed?" she repeated, making sure she knew what I was asking.

I nodded my head.

"Oh, I...I, I don't know about him getting killed. I mean, that's hard. I do not know that I would have been okay with it, but I've heard that's what happens to child molesters. They get killed or really roughed up in prison. He was always a coward in my eyes. He didn't care about me. All he cared about was himself. I wanted to see him behind bars regardless."

I curiously looked at my mom and asked a question I never thought to ask before, "Could the police have gone after him in Mexico?"

"There wasn't much they could do at that point — not with where the investigation stood." She casually brushed this off, not allowing herself to get caught up in what never was. It was comforting to see how free my mom felt from the past. It made me feel free to ask her anything.

"Do you still think Valentina being molested was your fault?" I immediately felt guilty for asking, but felt like I needed to, and that this was no time for guilt.

My mom responded in a strong, confident manner without hesitation.

"I continue to feel a responsibility, however I know it is not my fault. I do feel that if I had done something sooner, it would not have happened — but there is no use in taking on guilt which is so detrimental to one's own health and healing. I was going through a strenuous time and I was losing it mentally. You heard me a lot at the house, screaming and crying. I was a mess and truly going crazy."

"What did you do to stay sane?" I asked my mom, amazed at her resilience and stability today. She paused for a few seconds to ponder her survival.

"I figured I just needed to move on. I started therapy, talking about it as much as I could to others, repeatedly went to my safe space to speak with God, and would take off on spiritual retreats as often as I could. There was so much to balance — you kids, your dad, the house, my job — and I felt like I didn't really have support. You were all too young and your dad didn't really know what to do. It was awkward for him. Daniel was not well because of all the physical and mental injury he sustained from our father, and the others simply could not handle the truth of who our parents really were.

"I also threw myself into my kids' lives, keeping us all busy with activities I never got the chance to do as a kid. I really cherished the communities I was building along the way. I became the vice president of your elementary school, the Girl Scout leader of your troops, the receptionist at the gymnastics gym you guys trained at, the Spanish teacher of your grade school, amongst other commitments. I did the best I could to offer you guys a life unlike my own.

"Every once in a while, I was able to discuss the abuse with your dad, but he didn't know what to say. He was having his own struggle with it. Thinking back, I'm glad I wrote that letter to him before we got married. At least it was never a secret between us." She smiled lovingly at my dad.

I looked at my dad's kind face and wondered if he ever thought he would have these conversations with his children. If so, was it anything like he expected? He opened up his heart.

"After hearing the news that your abuelitos fled to Mexico, I thought, *Yes! He's gone! We don't have to worry about it anymore. My problems, our problems, are gone!* Little did I realize there were serious mental and physical repercussions we still needed to address. I had no idea how to begin working through and coping with all the trauma. We needed to surrender to life's terms, and that is not the easiest thing to do. I could not predict how all of this would affect me or my children. The worst part was your abuelito was in our lives for many years after we got married. I do not know why we allowed that to…"

He trailed off before starting again, fixated on this, one of his greatest regrets. "That is the part that bugs me to no end. The part where I didn't say, 'Let's keep your parents out of our lives.' Why did we allow them around our kids? It just blows my mind. I know a person like that does not change easily. I often tell your mom that, in hindsight, we should have gotten married and left California. We should have gone someplace far away where we would never have to see them again. But it's easy to see that now. I just wish I would have had a little more strength and wisdom back then to make that decision for my family. But I didn't, and we stayed." His voice began to shake, "I gave him the benefit of the doubt. I was young, dumb, and thought your mom was the only one he abused. I know now that you should never give the benefit of the doubt to a child molester. Ever. No matter who they are in your life."

I imagined my parents' strife, knowing the decisions they made, or avoided making, led to their oldest daughter's molestation. Coming to terms with that horror would be a challenge for everyone in my immediate family. But more than anything, it would be a process for my sister, my mom, and my dad to work through individually and together.

During Valentina's teenage years, she felt anger to the point of resentment towards our parents, feeling they failed to protect her. Neither my sister, brother, nor I, knew the extent of our mother's story or our father's anguish and confusion. It would be a long winding road to learn that life has no plan or rules, regardless of your parents' desire to protect you.

Valentina was the final thread pulled in the unraveling of Abuelito Hector's rotting empire. She had, without knowing it, helped begin to undo our ancestral trauma. My abuelitos' lives were never the same, and for the better, neither were ours.

22

As 1995 drew to a close, a little over a year and a half after my mom and her brothers confronted their parents in Purepero, our families were entering the new year hopeful. As tradition held, our families were to gather at Tío Leo and Tía Emma's house to ring in 1996. It would be the second New Year's Eve celebration without Abuelito Hector and Abuelita Carmen. Little did our family know, another crisis was about to hit.

Tía Jessica had the sharpest memory of what happened on December 31st, 1995. She shared this with me amidst the burning sage and crystals, and the photos of her and Tío Samuel peppered throughout her house. She grabbed the bowl of sage and wafted its smoke over both our bodies.

"We were driving to Leo and Emma's for the party when we came to a red light. I put lipstick on and Samuel told me how beautiful I looked," she smiled, "and I blew him a kiss. The light turned green and when we approached the intersection Samuel shouted, 'Oh shhhhhh…!' I turned to look at him but all I saw was a white flash."

Their car went flying through the air, hitting the asphalt with a deafening thud. Jessica whipped her seatbelt off and threw herself into the back seat to check on the kids. They were badly injured, but alive. Realizing Samuel was not in the car, she looked around, confused. Finally, she spotted him lifeless on the street and rushed over to him. Screaming, she fell to the ground. As she held him in her arms, the chaos around them faded into the distance. They focused only on each other.

Samuel drifted between consciousness and the tempting white light that death brings with it. Jessica reassured her husband, "Babe, we got into a really bad accident. I want you to know it's not your fault." She looked at Samuel adoringly, knowing he would not be alive for much longer, and savored their every last second together.

She would never regret being able to say goodbye. Though it would be the most tragic experience of her life, she was eternally grateful to be with him during his final breaths. The couple lay in the street together, Jessica whispering, "I love you," as Samuel faded away.

Jessica's heart shattered, helicopters flew above, and people gathered, looking on with shock and terror.

Samuel Madero was a professional boxer and was up for the world title in the light-heavyweight category. He was slated to fight Virgil Hill in the spring of 1996, entering the ring to his epic walk-out song of choice: Queen's "We Will Rock You," with the hopes of a win to then play Queen's "We Are the Champions." Jessica knew he would have been champion. He was always hers.

While Jessica held Samuel on the street that day, Esperanza was at home making carnitas and rice to take over to Leo's house for the party. She got a panicked call from Leo explaining that Samuel and the family were in a car accident and he was on his way to the scene. Leo told his sister he would call once he got there, but made it sound not too bad, since he did not yet have all the details. Esperanza waited, becoming increasingly nervous. When Ricardo returned from the store, Esperanza relayed to him what she knew. Ricardo decided to go to the scene himself and call her with news.

Esperanza anxiously awaited updates at home, cooking to get her mind off of worst-case scenarios. Finally, she heard cars in the driveway and saw Ricardo and Leo pulling up at the same time. She ran outside and Ricardo took the kids to the playroom while Leo stayed with his sister on the front steps.

"What's happening? What's going on?" Esperanza asked Leo in desperation.

"Samuel died," Leo said abruptly and sadly, feeling the devastation move through his body. It was the heaviest news he ever told his sister.

"No! No! Let's go back! We have to do CPR! Leo, please!" she pleaded.

Leo softly took his sister by the shoulders, locked eyes with her and said, "Esperanza. He's gone," but she could not accept what she was hearing.

"No! That can't be! We have to go help him! Please, Leo, let's go!"

"Sis, he's gone. He's really gone," Leo pushed his voice through lumps in his throat, and in that instant, Esperanza let out an excruciating shrill of a scream from the depths of her soul, as if it were escaping her, defeated by a life of treachery. She fell to her knees. Leo joined her, hugging her tightly as they sobbed for their brother, gone too soon.

I was only nine when Tío Samuel passed, but I remember it vividly. My dad gathered my sister, brother, and me together in the playroom, and kneeled down to meet our eyes. He cried, delivering the news, explaining to us that Tío Samuel was in a bad accident and was now in heaven. He brought us in close and hugged us while we cried, hugging us tighter as our mom's scream shook us to our core, experiencing the weight of death's heartache for the first time.

The torment of hearing her best friend and nearly twin of a brother was gone overpowered her. My mom and Tío Samuel were inseparable growing up. Other than my dad, he was her greatest support through the trauma with their father, constantly expressing to her how much he loved her. She could not believe he was gone.

...All because a police officer was trying to catch kids accused of stealing from another man's van. The officer engaged in a high-speed chase, reaching over 100 mph, flying through the suburban streets of Huntington Beach, California. The fatal error was the cop's: he forgot to turn on his siren, failing to alert the cars on the road that they were coming — and fast.

It was when the two young adults and cop blew through a red light that they crashed into Tío Samuel and Tía Jessica's Jeep, ejecting Tío Samuel from the driver's seat window, landing him on the pavement, while Tía Jessica and the kids tumbled in the car.

The brothers called their parents in Mexico to inform them of Samuel's death. Devastated by the loss of their son, Hector and Carmen insisted on attending the funeral — and facing the children they deserted.

Later, at the hospital, Leo entered Jessica's room apprehensively to let her know of his parents' inevitable arrival and his father's desire to be a pallbearer. The news added to her torment, but she understood Samuel was their son. She shook her head in a state of contempt and told Leo that her in-laws were not allowed to speak to or touch her children. She spent all those years being nice to them for Samuel, and now he was gone. She no longer had to show them respect when she had none for them. She did not love them. They were awful people. She would not be rude to them, but she would outright ignore them.

Leo understood completely and nodded in agreement.

Twelve hundred people attended Samuel's funeral, not including the reporters and news vans. The sheer size of the crowd in all black was a profound testament to Samuel's character and how many lives he touched. He was a remarkable soul, and many people would miss him. The funeral itself was beautiful, with family and friends overflowing outside of the church doors into the lobby. Esperanza settled in the front of the church while people walked up to offer their condolences. Jessica took the podium to honor her husband with words of praise and mourning. Esperanza was locked on her, amazed at how courageous and strong she was, getting up in front of a mass of people to speak in the midst of tremendous suffering.

After a dignified burial, and the reception at the church hall, a smaller group gathered at Ricardo and Esperanza's home for an intimate family reception. When Jessica arrived, her first sight was Hector and Carmen seated on the couch. They locked eyes for a second, but she turned her head quickly and kept on walking. When she made it to the backyard, she plopped down next to Daniel and Leo and cracked open a beer. It was all too much.

What if the cop had sounded his sirens, minding the safety of his community? This is the *what if* my family lives with, as we try to liberate ourselves from this dangerous and delusional line of thinking. Meanwhile, the officer and the sole survivor of the kids car have lived with their careless actions of that day.

I hope these individuals have forgiven themselves, but more so, I hope they have taken what is sure to be their gravest error in life and used it to make themselves better people, and an exceptionally better police officer. I hope all police officers think sincerely about what it truly means to protect and serve, for this job has taken too many lives needlessly. I hope more work is done to separate the man from the ego in this loaded line of work. I hope all the officers who have already done this mental work, and do it daily, lead the way.

"We Are The Champions"
Queen

I've paid my dues
Time after time.
I've done my sentence
But committed no crime.

And bad mistakes—
I've made a few.
I've had my share of sand kicked in my face
But I've come through.

And I need to go on and on, and on, and on.

We are the champions, my friends.
And we'll keep on fighting 'til the end.
We are the champions.
We are the champions.
No time for losers
'Cause we are the champions of the world.

23

The tragedy of Tío Samuel's loss hit the family like a missile, and Abuelito Hector and Abuelita Carmen's presence triggered complex emotions that the family worked hard to let go of. Yet, in times of loss, there is a tendency to reacquaint with our most tender selves. The shared heartache of losing Tío Samuel caused my family to put their differences aside, even if only briefly.

Sipping on a beer in Tío Leo's family room, I let myself sink into the sofa as I listened to him speak.

"It was a heavy time for everybody. I won't lie, it was uncomfortable with my parents back in town. We were all in mourning though, and I can't imagine anyone would deny parents the right to bury their child. I was not angry at them during this time because it was not about me, and I was not looking to be angry. I was just trying to get through losing my brother. I was glad my parents were able to bury their son, but if they hadn't come, it would not have changed anything in my life. I won't say I was happy to see them. To this day I have not missed them. They hurt one of the people I love the most."

My sister went through a confusing experience seeing abuelito during this time. As we savored our red wine, she reflected on how distorted she was at the time, when she was just 10 years old.

"Abuelito and Abuelita had just pulled up and they were about to walk into the house, and Mami quickly pulled me aside and said, 'Mija, I want you to know your abuelito Hector is here.' I turned around, saw him, and my first reaction was excitement. That goes to show how confusing these things are for a little kid, and how easy it is for an adult to prey on them.

"Anyways, I ran to him, hugged him, and mid-hug I thought, *Wooooaaah! Wait a minute, I do not feel right about this hug. Why do I not feel right about this hug?*

"Suddenly there was this overwhelming sense of guilt and shame that crept in and filled my heart for decades. There was a lot of confusion in my mind around *What is good? What is bad? What did it mean that my instinct was still affection towards this man?*

"I let go of him and walked away, not saying another word to him for the rest of the day. The reality is, people do not want to talk about sexual abuse. It is never easy to navigate. There are a lot of emotions involved in making the decision to speak out, and I held onto shame for many years. It is natural to feel guilt, shame, fear, and many other emotions — it's just sad that this is the natural cycle of trauma for the survivor. The shame belongs to the predator, yet the individuals abused are the ones who feel it the most."

I thought of the innocence of a child, and the psychological warfare that molestation inflicts to dismantle that innocence. Thanks to therapy and the support of her community, my sister found the courage to speak out, began mending her wounds, and has grown into a strong woman with a beautiful soul. But access to these tools are far too limited. As is the fortitude to use them even if you do have access.

From the quiet of their garden, my parents elaborated on this heavy time.

"My father came back to the United States only once, for Samuel's funeral," revealed my mom. "That morning was terrible all on its own, and then to top it off, my parents were in town. I was numb. Some people talked to them and gave their condolences, others did not acknowledge them at all, while others decided against attending the family reception because they knew my parents would be there. That was hard, but many of my friends pitched in to make the reception happen, and when we arrived after the services, the house was transformed. All the Christmas decorations were gone and the house was ready with food, drinks, and everything else you'd need to host a gathering. I was amazed and grateful, and I tried to focus on that."

"In the midst of everything," my dad recalled, "I forgot your abuelito was going to be there. It did not feel nice to have him there, and it was not a pleasant vibe. I was reliving instances I did not want to relive, so the minute your abuelitos left, life was somewhat back to normal. Only somewhat because pain like that does not just go away when that person disappears. You begin asking yourself all sorts of questions. *What happened?*

Why did I allow this? There are many unknowns on one's quest of rebuilding, and only you can answer those questions for yourself."

Later on, in the comfort of another home, my mom and I enjoyed a Tía Victoria snack specialty: tortillas with refried beans. From her and Tío Joel's dining room, we nibbled while Tía Victoria recalled her run-in with her former best friend at our house that day.

"I went into the front room and greeted Carmen. She told me: 'I knew you wouldn't fail me, Victoria. I knew you would greet me.' I felt bad for her. She thought I was going to sit with her, but no. I never sat down with her."

Tío Joel sipped on his tea and acknowledged, "We did go up to them and give our condolences. I felt horrible for my sister. Her son had just died. I gave her a long hug and forgot about their sins for a short while in order to be with them. Hector offered me a beer but I said, 'No thank you." Tío Joel shrugged his shoulders and shook his head.

Tía Victoria spoke as she served us, "When we were leaving, Carmen was outside and I finally gave her my hand to hold, telling her, 'For your son. Goodbye.'"

"Once we left them, it was back to the same attitude, with the same resentment," Tio Joel said matter-of-factly.

A much needed quiet moment swept through the dining room as we reflected individually on our family's past.

On a park bench next to me, Tía Elsa shook her head in disgust: "I cannot talk to your grandma. I'm angry and hurt. You do anything to fight for your children! You gave birth to your children! You give your life for your children! For her not to have done that — I don't want to have any words with her. If I did, they wouldn't be nice."

"What would you want to say to her?" I asked curiously, wanting to hear for myself, but also hoping that speaking the words out loud would be healing for her.

"First of all, I'm angry. Why did you flee? Why did you not stay with your children? Why did you allow your husband to do this to my cousin? She is your daughter! Did it not hurt you? What happened to you that you allowed your husband to hurt Esperanza and Daniel the way he did? Was it the money that kept you from saying anything?

"If you knew what kind of husband you had," she kept going, I didn't want to stop her, "why did you allow us to spend the night at your house? Why did you not confide in my dad or Tía Miranda? They're your siblings, and they adored you! They would have helped you! Why did you not put your foot down? I put a lot of blame on you for everything that happened."

Tía Elsa took a deep breath as she raised her eyebrows and smiled, "I don't know how she would react if I asked her all of that! I can't say all the bad words I want to say because…"

We cracked up, knowing she was censoring her words around me, still seeing me as the little girl I was when all this happened.

She resumed, "My mom and dad cried a lot, but my dad cried more. He considered your grandpa his brother, his best friend, and father figure. Any good thing you can say about a man, my dad would say about Hector, and to top it all off, this man was married to his sister. My dad would cry and say, 'I lost a sister, a brother, and my best friends.'

"Your abuelito should have gone to prison! Your abuelita should have gone to prison, too. That is what should have happened." Anger fueled Tía Elsa as the pace of her speech picked up. "If your abuelita really cared, she would not have let us nieces spend the night. When our parents said no, she would say, 'Let them stay. Let them stay,' even though she knew what kind of a monster her husband was and what he might do to us. I thought she was a good person. I loved her a lot. I really did. The day she passes away, if I'm still here, I do not want to know because to me she's already dead."

Her feelings were valid and shared by many.

"It was not just your abuelito, but your abuelita as well who damaged many people's lives. I would have talked to her, but because she fled, I was mad and didn't feel the need to anymore. Still don't. It really bothers me because your mom is such a good person and has such a good heart. She is always willing to help everybody, even though she lived the life she did, and went so long without the help she needed. That makes me sad. But it makes me happy to know someone as strong and pure hearted as her is a part of my life."

On another day, from the street they grew up on, my mom and Tía Jasmine stood next to me, staring at one of the many houses they were molested in. Our heads tilted in contemplative unison as Tía Jasmine shared her thoughts.

"When your grandpa came back into town for the funeral, we could have gone to the police and they would have immediately held him for questioning, but many of us talked about it before and agreed it was not an appropriate time. There was a lot of media surrounding Samuel's death, and I did not want news about your grandpa to get in the way of honoring Samuel's life."

We stood with the idea of him being held for questioning, daydreaming an alternate reality.

24

It was the year 2000, and much of the world was settling down from the scare of the digital world imploding. At fourteen years old, I was just getting to know myself. With holidays and summer vacations split between California and Purepero, I was making lasting memories and honoring traditions.

I learned how precious Mexican novelas are to my heart because they gathered my family together. I learned that family means being friends with the ones you love, even if you have drastically different approaches to life. In the case of me and my cousins, it meant being best friends and deepening our connections with age. I celebrated *Día de los Muertos* and learned what it meant to stay connected to the spirits of loved ones passed. I learned how to pray with a rosary, because my paternal abuelitos would have it no other way.

I ran around on my family's pig farm helping deliver piglets, with the understanding that they would be killed when the time came to put them on our plates — I even killed one myself for my paternal abuelitos' 50th wedding anniversary. I played hide-and-go seek in their backyard cornfield, and learned what it meant to fall in love for the first time. After savoring the joy of spending this time with these most cherished relatives, I surrendered to the heartache of leaving them when it came time to return to California. My body memorized the delicious smells, sights, and sounds of Mexico, deeply ingraining them into my psyche and my whole being. I refused to allow Abuelito Hector to make Purepero a place of terror for me, so I put him out of my mind and held onto the magic of my family's hometown.

Abuelito Hector and Abuelita Carmen took the liberty of taking half of Abuelita Elena's home, tearing it down, and building their house adjacent to hers. She didn't have an option. Her son's merciless domination did not stop with his mother. The two houses were now touching. There was no escaping Abuelito Hector's proximity.

My parents were always with me and my siblings during our visits to Abuelita Elena's home, keeping an eye on who walked through the front door. My siblings and I kept a relationship with Abuelita Carmen throughout the years, and she would come to Abuelita Elena's house and visit with us, never failing to bring us lavish home-cooked meals and gifts. She never missed a visit, though my mom kept her distance. My parents simply busied themselves in other rooms to avoid speaking while giving Abuelita Carmen time with her grandchildren. Abuelito Hector on the other hand, was forbidden to come anywhere near us, and surprisingly he obeyed, but we always knew he was mere feet away. Being alone with Abuelita Carmen was never the issue, it was being alone with Abuelito Hector or both of them together that was the problem. It wasn't until we were old enough to cruise the streets of Purepero ourselves that we visited Abuelita Elena on our own. On those later visits, we largely forgot about Abuelito Hector, regardless of his proximity. One of our main domains was Abuelita Isabella and Abuelito Antonio's home, my paternal grandparents, home, a several-minute walk away from my mother's parents. They served the role of grandparents with dignity, unlike their counterparts.

Over the years, the loneliness inside Hector's and Carmen's souls began to hollow them. Their children barely spoke to them, barely visited, and those who did, did so awkwardly, while most of their grandchildren rarely saw them at all.

Valentina turned 15 which meant it was time for her quinceañera — an event vital for any Mexican abuelita to attend. Carmen decided she would travel back to the states to be there. It had been four years since she was last in Huntington Beach for her son's funeral, and Esperanza was feeling nervous to have her back in town.

Esperanza decided to take the opportunity to sit face-to-face with her mother and get answers to the questions that had been tormenting her for decades. It would be the last trip her mother made back to the U.S. for fourteen years.

Carmen arrived in California, staying with Fernando and his family. Sitting in their dining room, she awaited her daughter's arrival, knowing a challenging conversation loomed overhead. Anxious and hopeful,

Esperanza walked into her brother's house, her body filling with nausea. Gloria, Fernando's wife, was there for support and to serve as a witness in case Carmen tried changing the story of what took place. Gloria stood a favorable distance away in the kitchen, giving the mother and daughter the space they needed.

Esperanza took a seat directly across from her mother, who sat perfectly still with a stern poker face. With a deep breath, she launched into a diatribe about the sexual abuse she endured at her father's behest, diving deeper into details than she ever had before. Carmen's face morphed into worry as she turned her gaze to her daughter-in-law and then back to her daughter, concerned a third party was now fully aware of her and her husband's crimes — always more concerned with how outsiders perceived her than the ones she called her own.

"Why did you allow it?" Esperanza's face was fiery with determination, ready for a better outcome without her father around, but her mother stared back stone-cold.

"Why did you send me to your bedroom knowing he was in there nude?" Esperanza asked. Her mother responded only with silence.

"Why did you make me bring him dinner to your bedroom if you knew he was going to molest me?!" Esperanza grew agitated at her mother's blank expression, and became louder, firing questions that dropped like bombs.

"Why did you have me give him massages when you knew he was only wearing underwear and you knew what he was going to do to me? Why?! Answer me!" Esperanza shouted.

"Why did you do nothing about it?! Why were you complicit?!" Esperanza stared at her mother, hoping for an answer, tears, anything but silence. But silence was all she got. A lump grew in her throat and she yearned for her mother to throw her a lifeline.

"Aren't you going to say anything?!" Esperanza pleaded with a mix of resentment and hope. To her surprise, her mother finally allowed words to come out.

"What do you want me to say?" Carmen asked her daughter, holding her icy stare.

Esperanza erupted, "Mom! If you tell me you were afraid of Dad, or he was threatening you in some way, I'll understand! You have got to tell me something! Why did you not leave him?" Esperanza demanded an answer.

Carmen answered truthfully. "I did not know what to do. What would I have done with five kids?"

Esperanza, relieved yet unsatisfied with her mother's response, shot back, "Gosh! You could have reached out for help or financial aid. You could have asked your siblings! Why did you not ask them for help?"

Carmen resorted back to quiet.

Tears slowly rolled down Esperanza's cheeks. "I cannot believe you will not tell me something to at least ease my pain or help me cope. I don't want to continue thinking that you had a part in all this. I'm hoping there is something I am missing." Esperanza was giving her mother an opening to come clean and explain herself, so they could potentially start over, so Esperanza could forgive her, which she so desperately wanted to do. She gave her mom ample time to answer before pushing her again.

"Mom?"

Yet again, Carmen answered, "What do you want me to say?"

Esperanza felt the pain of a dagger enter her heart while her mother twisted the blade, killing what little hope she had left for resolution. She dropped her head in defeat. She was not missing anything. She longed for an apology, or sincere remorse, but received nothing close. With a deep breath, she locked eyes with her mother and proclaimed, "This is it. I cannot see you or talk to you anymore. I need you out of my life. Goodbye, Mom."

Carmen's face remained blank and guilty. Through the thickness of the deafening quiet, Esperanza got up from the table, wiped her tears, and walked out the front door.

"That was it," my mom proclaimed. "My brothers and I asked her never to come back. It was excruciating to hear her responses — or complete lack thereof — so we told her we never wanted her to visit us again.

"It was hard for all of us to have her back in town. After she left, she called every once in a while, and then two years later in 2002 she called to ask why she was not being invited to your quinceañera. I simply told her it was too hard for me to see her. She insisted everything was fine between us, and that she had a right to be there. She tried to make me feel guilty, so I just stopped answering her calls. She would leave messages, but I never returned them.

"One year, she left a message saying, 'Are you ever going to answer my calls?' I can still picture it, standing in the kitchen, mail in hand, staring at the answering machine listening to her voice. It was too hard to speak to my parents. My insomnia would get worse when I did, so for many years I cut them out of my life completely. I did it for my own health! I would see them by coincidence when we visited Purepero, but it was always at a distance and I would make a U-turn and walk the other way.

"Over time, I tried to understand why she did nothing to help me or Daniel, like tell someone or get a job and get us out of there. I guess she felt like the doors closed on her, but I know her siblings would have helped if she had the courage to ask. She could have worked, maybe caring for kids..."

My mom paused and we erupted in laughter at the absurdity of her final statement, and she quickly added, "I guess caring for kids would not have been the right job, but she could have found something. We could have been on welfare for a bit until we were able to get on our feet. It is not like we would have fallen off the face of the earth. One of her siblings would have taken us in! I know there were a lot of us and it would have been chaotic, but considering the type of emergency it was, her siblings would have gladly helped. There is always a solution, you just have to look for it."

The years brought with them a natural progression of internal harmony, with the natural range of emotions: animosity, love, resentment, joy, hope, hopelessness, regret, and so many others. Over time, my mom found the strength to forgive her parents. She cannot point to a specific moment of clarity, rather, she sees her entire journey as the path of forgiveness. Speaking about her trauma on weekend retreats helped make traditional talk therapy easier, and helped speed up her recovery. Coming to terms with her right to separate from them and keep her father and mother out of her life was an important step. Although accepting this was grueling, she knew it needed to happen. They abused her, and they abused their titles as mother and father — she had the power to rescind their role in her life.

There was no more sense to make of this mess. Forgiving her parents was the healthiest way forward for herself and her family. Although she wrestled with anger for a long time, she fought hard against allowing it to overpower her. And so, moment by moment, as best she could, she let the light in.

Everyone in the family approached their path to forgiveness in
different ways, and inside me grew a burning desire to face my biggest fear:
Abuelito Hector.

My mom and I drove around Huntington Beach recording stories for
the book, slurping our sodas, and listening to the Beatles' "All the Lonely
People" playing on the radio:
'Eleanor Rigby, died in the church
And was buried along with her name
Nobody came
Father McKenzie, wiping the dirt
From his hands as he walks from the grave
No one was saved
All the lonely people
Where do they all come from?
All the lonely people
Where do they all belong?'

Daydreaming in the passenger seat, I substituted my abuelito for
Eleanor Rigby, fantasizing the day he would lay lifeless in a coffin. Just
then, a thought popped into my head and I voiced it aloud.
"Tío Daniel told me that after your parents fled he went to Mexico to
live with them so he could go and..."
"Hurt them. Not physically, just emotionally," my mom said, taking
over. She knew better than anyone the misery her brother felt and the
desire to bring revenge upon those who inflicted it. "He wanted the
community to know our parents were not these great people to aspire to
— that they caused agonizing heartache for him and our whole family. He
lived with our parents in Mexico for about a year. He was just trying to deal
with the hardships of life."
"That's right!" I exclaimed, recalling when he personally told me this in
high school. My friend and I had been hanging out with Tío Daniel after
school, playing board games, snacking, and talking the afternoon away. Tío
Daniel looked at us with a smirk and let us in on why he went to live with
his parents.
"The only reason I did it, Mija, was because I wanted to punish them
and cause them deep pain. I wanted everyone to know we were not this
perfect family my parents wanted them to think we were. It was my way of
getting back at them," Tío Daniel explained.

He felt an obvious sense of satisfaction. I admired him for living through what he did and having the courage to confront his parents in adulthood, under the same roof. I was not sure what actions he took against them, but I was not there to judge.

Everyone's inner journey to peace and mental stability is different and personal. I would never be able to fully comprehend what Tío Daniel went through. All I could do was accept and support his path to healing. His father and mother failed to provide a nurturing environment for him, and thus he fell into constant despair and distrust. Despite this, he was a vibrant soul, and was especially affectionate with his nieces and nephews, always good for a smile, a laugh, and a lesson.

Tío Daniel's searing desire to confront his parents with his own anguish made me think of my own desire. I used to dream of the day I would stand in front of Abuelito Hector and the powerful words I would say. Throughout the years, I built, tore apart, and rebuilt the perfectly daggered statement to pierce him with. I felt in my bones that I would be face-to-face with him one day, I just did not know when or what it would look like. When the time finally came, it did not go quite as planned. Looking back, how could it have?

"Remember when I told you about my confrontation with Abuelito?" I asked my mom while she drove.

"Mhmm," muttered my mom, nodding her head with a slight smile.

We pulled up to my mom's safe space, and staring off into the distance, where the palm trees met the sky, I thought back to my own determination and courage that day.

It was December 31st, 2005 in Purepero, Michoacán, and I was 19 years old. The town's main plaza was full of life. Bright lights and fireworks illuminated the night sky, allowing for glimpses of the mountains that surrounded the town. Shouts and laughter bounced off the adobe walls as crowds of people gathered to celebrate the new year. Food vendors lined the streets with two and a half hours left until midnight. I was surrounded by some of my favorite people — my siblings and cousins — and everywhere I looked I saw smiles and happiness, yet I felt empty. Ever since Tío Samuel's death, New Years had become a somber and for the most part un-celebrated holiday in our family. Even throughout my teenage years, New Years Eve never felt quite like a celebration. From the plaza, I felt a sudden urge to get up and run.

I stood up from my bench, slowly and without notice walked towards some quieter, sleepier streets, slipping away from the lights and laughter. I immediately felt lighter and let out a big exhale. Purepero is small and I know my way around, so without reflecting much, I headed towards Abuelita Carmen and Abuelito Hector's house. I felt I was pushed along by the slightest of winds, moving alongside the outlines of the mountains against a dark starry sky.

I always stayed with my paternal abuelitos or cousins when in Purepero and felt as at home there as I did in Huntington Beach. I had never even been inside Abuelito Hector's and Abuelita Carmen's home in Purepero. Valentina, Ricky, and I snuck in as curious young kids once when our abuelitos were not home, but only explored a couple rooms before chickening out and jumping back over the fence back to Abuelita Elena's home.

On this New Year's Eve, I felt compelled to step inside with both of them there and confront my abuelito and my fear. I felt safe knowing Abuelita Elena was right next door, and that as he aged, Abuelito Hector was growing weaker and more frail — because I had to consider the possibility of the situation escalating to me needing to physically overpower him. Knowing everything I knew about what he was capable of, I could not underestimate his reaction.

Before I fully accepted what I was about to do, I was standing in front of their door. I tried to talk myself out of ringing the doorbell and debated whether to simply turn back and rejoin my family, or go in and face the man I built my fear around. I stood outside their home for 15 minutes, trying to summon the courage to ring the bell. My hands were shaking, my heart pounding, and my insides felt like they were trying to claw their way out, my legs too weak to hold me up. Why did I decide to do this now? I was not sure, something deep within piloted me here.

Although I had seen him several times walking the streets of our hometown, I was about to speak with Abuelito Hector for the first time in over a decade. Typically, if I saw him from afar, I would avoid him, though my heart would begin to race and anxiety would take over my body.

I started to cry, my breathing became heavy, and my stomach felt as if it was slowly melting. I felt I was about to faint and throw up at the same time. I needed to get myself together. I jumped up, shook my head, wiggled my arms and legs, wiped my tears, took a deep breath, and rang the doorbell — all in what seemed like one fluid motion before I could talk myself out of it.

The sound of my abuelita's voice on the intercom shattered the blaring pounding of my own heartbeat: "Hello?" she said curiously.

"Hey abuelita, it's me, Amelia," I answered.

"Oh mija! How great it is to hear your voice. Wait there. I'm coming!"

I could hear her excitement that I came to visit, and I knew she was smiling from ear to ear. Oddly enough, so was I, as I waited for Abuelita Carmen's laugh and warm embrace.

She was always loving with my siblings and me, even though she was not nearly as affectionate with her own daughter. I guess it was easier with her grandchildren.

She squealed excitedly as she swung the front door open, hugging me tightly, crying and laughing at the same time. She led me through the entryway and up a big set of stairs that took you into the house. I stepped inside and time came rushing at me. The past and present colliding, stopping inches from my body, before slamming into me. I got a head rush and goosebumps, feeling both out of my element and oddly comfortable.

Much of the furniture and small knick-knacks were items Abuelita Carmen and Abuelito Hector shipped from California when they fled the country, and it took me right back to my childhood. Massive paintings of angels and the traditional Mexican image of the warrior Popocatépetl carrying his beloved princess Iztaccíhuatl hung on the walls. Pictures of my cousins and I were everywhere. Everywhere. Most of them were of us as kids, and they lined every surface, frame after frame — an homage to the memories of children and grandchildren who no longer came to visit, no longer called to talk.

The house was beautiful but eerie and I felt dizzy. I was spiraling backwards. My head rush became a throat rush and I kept needing to take big breaths to regulate my body. Abuelita Carmen was just as nervous. She decided to give me a tour of the house, and I wondered which cave he was hiding in.

We started in the living room. I took my time, stopping to stare at each picture. I picked up the porcelain dolls and remembered how much I loved them as a kid, and made my way over to admire the tall wooden grandfather clock whose chime echoed in my youth. I skimmed my fingers over the mini ceramic Christmas tree, its lights blinking off and on, as they had for infinite holiday seasons. I walked past the bottom of the stairs, standing at the hand-carved wooden bar that people no longer gathered at, into the dining room with the yellow velvet chairs no one had eaten at in ages.

I took it all in and let myself drop into nostalgia, feeling harmoniously high. I wanted to see every inch of the place, feeling like a beautiful part of my history was robbed from me by this bad man. I slowly wandered into the bathroom, Abuelita Carmen following a few steps behind, smiling, afraid to break the spell of the visit. I told her how beautiful the shell on her bathroom sink was and without letting a second pass she picked it up and put it in my hands.

"It's yours," she said. Anytime I told her I liked something, a memento or decorative object, she said it was mine to have. I could feel her desperately trying to make up for the past.

We drifted into the kitchen and she asked if I wanted milk and cookies. Her face lit up with my desire. I could see in her eyes this was all she wanted, to simply be an abuelita. I never knew how much it meant for a grandmother to serve her grandchild milk and cookies. Though I did not miss out on these experiences — I had them with Abuelita Elena and Abuelita Isabella — but I could sense Abuelita Carmen was craving the connection. The package of cookies had never been opened, waiting on top of the fridge for an opportunity like this. I felt suddenly aware of and very grateful for both the simplicity and the magnitude of this moment.

Standing around with my hands in my pockets, I looked up and circled the kitchen to examine every knick-knack. I finally sat down to enjoy my treat, letting the cookies bridge the connection between me and her. The fuzzy sensation in my head moved down my body, flooding my bones with a nervous chill. It was odd to feel so at home, and yet so far away. After some quality time, she wanted to show me the rest of the house, so we continued the tour. We walked past a closed bedroom door, where I figured he must be, down a long hallway and out onto the back patio. Their clothes hung out to dry on a line, giving company to the trees and plants that flourished. It was dark out, but nice and quiet. We stood for a bit, basking in the serenity before walking back inside. When we reached the stairs, it took us several minutes to make our way up, stopping at nearly every step to examine the artwork on the walls. She and I both knew we were stalling.

For the first time in a long time, the sense of being present overwhelmed me. She showed me through every room, and it was a big house. Pictures of all our families hung in the bedrooms, rarely used or slept in. She killed time by telling me stories, becoming more and more nervous knowing there was one last bedroom to see.

As we walked back down the stairs and approached the master bedroom, she stopped and stared at me before asking, "Are you sure you want to go inside?"

"Yes," I quickly responded.

She looked at me concerned, "Your abuelito is in the room. Are you sure you still want to go in?"

Once again, I quickly answered yes. Abuelita Carmen slowly opened the door to the unlit room. "Hector, Amelia and I are coming in and turning on the light. Cover your face."

She flicked the light on, and I took a deep breath as I saw the outline of his body under the sheets. I felt an unexpected sense of sympathy for him. He was hiding from the whole world. Abuelita Carmen and I walked right past him, through the master bedroom and into the bathroom, shutting the door behind us. She was shaky but carried on showing me the stained-glass window and other upgrades she'd made in her years of isolation. In the middle of showing me her walk-in closet, she broke down. My own attempts to hold it together failed miserably.

Every emotion I was trying to contain exploded and I began to cry uncontrollably. Abuelita Carmen and I held each other until our eyes ran dry. She gave me a small pack of tissues and told me to blow my nose before taking my hand tightly into hers and walking towards the door and back into the bedroom.

Once again, all I saw was the outline of his body lying in bed, the sheets still over his head. I was nervous but somehow was able to spit out, "Abuelito, can I talk to you?"

His body tensed up at the sound of my voice, and my head started spinning, *Why do you want to talk to him, Amelia? What are you going to say? What are you going to ask?*

I was not sure, but I was running on adrenaline and inexplicably ready. I may never get this chance again.

He slowly removed the sheet from his face as I walked over to his bedside, trying to let the uneasiness in my body pass. He was skinnier than I remembered and much more pale, with his eyes sunken in. It was a couple years since I last saw him walking the streets, and again I could feel a lump in my throat forming and tears ready to flow, but I refused to let them. I stared at him forcefully, and he stared right back. I stood above him for what felt like several minutes, locked in and breathing deeply.

My emotions intensified. I stared harder and pushed the tears back further until they no longer posed a threat to my composure. I took big gulps and swallowed the lump in my throat until it was gone. I could feel my body temperature skyrocket and plummet in quick succession, yet I remained confident.

To my own surprise, I sat on the edge of the bed only an arm's reach away from him. It felt surreal. I was face-to-face with my biggest fear. Face-to-face with the person I equated darkness and evil with, the source of all my anger. We stared, still not saying a word. Each silent second that passed relaxed me as I realized how weak he was. I got my bearings in the situation I put myself in and thought, *You can physically overpower him. Nothing to worry about. You are stronger. You got this.*

The first question finally came out of my mouth, "Why did you molest my mom?" He looked at me and with barely a hesitation responded, "I didn't."

His lie brought a sneer to my face, before he fired off more.

He said he couldn't understand how my mom could make all of this up. How he was always a great father and did not know why she would spread such horrid lies about him. I felt more sympathy and compassion for him with every lie he told. He would never change. The change I was seeking was up to me, and me alone. He was in a much darker, sinister world than I would ever be, and for that I felt sorry for him.

"What about Valentina and all your nieces? They say you molested them, too. Are you telling me that everyone is lying?" I pressed him.

"Yes. I did not do any of what they say," he responded calmly and comfortably.

I knew he may not admit to any of his actions. This conversation was for me, and me alone.

That did not stop me from interrogating him.

"Did you like the feeling of overpowering little girls? When did you first molest a child? Was my mom the first? Do you feel any empathy at all? Are you sorry for what you did?"

I peered over his frail body as he stuck to his story, denying he had anything to feel bad for. "I did not do anything wrong. None of it is true."

He tried victimizing himself, but it was easy to see through his manipulation. I laughed quietly out of frustration and disbelief, shaking my head. I completely forgot Abuelita Carmen was standing behind us, completely forgot about the entire world around me.

I repeated questions and demanded answers. I wanted to know why. Why did he do what he did? I wanted to push him to admit his heinous crimes. He didn't, but I felt powerful letting him know I didn't believe a single word he said. He lay and I sat, and we talked for forty-five minutes

— the longest stretch of time I had spoken to him since he fled nearly 12 years earlier.

Before walking into the house, I wanted to yell at him, cuss him out, tell him he was worthless, and throw my perfectly daggered statement at him, cutting him down. But as I heard him speak lie after lie, I felt the pit of my stomach churn my extreme ire to sympathy. It was the strangest feeling. I tried to imagine what kind of life he must have endured in order to turn out this way. To me, he was still a monster of a man, a pathetic villain deserving of nothing, but I couldn't help but feel bad for him. Curiously enough, I felt my heart soften.

I began to forgive him. I started to feel liberated. Every lie he told was like a brick being taken off from on top of me. One lie after another, denying he ever touched my mom, my sister, my tías, my mom's friends, or anyone else, when the effects of his actions were palpable by all. Still locked into his gaze, I felt the strange desire to hug him, look him straight in the eyes, and tell him I forgave him. I wanted him to hug me back and sincerely say he was sorry. I wanted him to cry.

He did not. I did not hug him either or tell him I forgave him. I started to forgive him on my own — although it would be a long road — and that was all I needed. The conversation was for me, not for him. I did not need his confession to heal. The healing had begun.

After hearing all the lies I could for one night, I stood up. "I'm sorry you cannot admit to what you've done. Goodbye, Abuelito." Abuelita Carmen walked out of the bedroom with me, shutting the door behind us before joining me in the living room.

I plopped down on the sofa and cried, and found my abuelita soon next to me, following suit. I lifted my head from my tear covered hands, locked eyes with her, and asked, "Why did you let it happen?"

She cried, holding my hands in hers, "Forgive me, mija, forgive me!"

She repeated this over and over while we hugged and cried. She asked me to tell my mom that she was sorry, which jarred me. Suddenly, I stopped crying and quickly shot back, "You need to be the one to tell her that!"

My frankness jolted her. "I know, I know," she said with big sad brown eyes. We allowed ourselves to sob, contemplating the part of us that did not want this strange night to end.

I was done. I wanted to go back to Abuelita Isabella's and Abuelito Antonio's and meet up with my family. I hugged Abuelita Carmen and walked with her to the front door. I felt sad but free. Walking away from their house that night, my spiritual and mental wellbeing began to shift, bending towards surrender. I walked away with a smile on my face, a shell in my hand, and a feeling of total weightlessness.

Street lamps lit the quiet, colorful road back to my paternal abuelitos' home. The several minute walk between my maternal and paternal grandparents' homes felt longer that night, allowing me to absorb what just took place.

Midnight struck while I was in that house, and on my way to a safer one, under a beautiful starry sky, I found myself laughing, smiling, skipping, twirling, and crying. From the outside, I looked unhinged. And I was! Unhinged from facing my biggest fear and processing. I danced with my face up towards the moon, my eyes halfway closed. The hatred and fear I held for so long were dissolving, and the winds of the night were sweeping in to take their fading remnants into the cosmos, where they would merge with other vibrations, until the emotions, as they once were, existed no longer.

I returned to my family celebrating the new year. My siblings and cousins all gathered in the kitchen, sipping their preferred drink to eventually put them to bed. Still intoxicated by the power of forgiveness, I frantically shared with them where I had just been, what I had just done. They were supportive, my biggest cheerleaders, and yet they felt the situation was unresolved. My sister, in particular, craved the feeling I was emitting — elation, vindication, pride. She decided she would go the next morning to do the same, her burning desire to grill Abuelito Hector stronger than ever.

Thirteen years later, my sister brought to mind that next morning. "My confrontation did not feel quite as freeing," Valentina spoke. "I walked into their home and sat down in the dining room on the yellow velvet chairs. Abuelito walked out of his room and into the bathroom, where he washed his hands, before coming to sit with me. I could see into the bathroom, and while I watched him wash his old wrinkly hands, it felt extraordinarily symbolic, like he was washing away his sins before coming to lie to me. He joined me at the table and I immediately fired questions at him.

'Were you ever molested?' I asked him.

He answered no and left it at that.

"I wanted to pry, but I was not in a mental state to do so. I asked him about Mami and he lied to me. It was then I thought, *I do not believe a word you are saying*. But not only did I not believe him, my vision of who he was and what he looked like changed. His nose, his eyes, his entire face looked different. It was clear all questions I asked would be met with a lie, but I couldn't stop myself, I wanted to interrogate him.

'Did you love us?' I finally asked. At that point, he started to cry, then so did I.

"Through his tears, he answered yes, and I just thought, *I wish I could believe that.* But I could not believe a single word. I stared him down, my thoughts cycling, question after question. *Really? You loved us? You just lied to me. How am I supposed to believe you? If you loved us, why did you do this? If you really loved us, why are you still lying?*

"I felt strangely similar to that day when I was a little girl at that birthday party — the day after I told Mami about the abuse for the first time. I was not feeling angry or fearful. I was not feeling much of anything to be honest, so I got up and walked out of the house. When I was outside I thought, *Wow! Amelia felt empowered and liberated. I feel trapped.*"

While I listened to Valentina, I was shocked, yet satisfied to hear Abuelito Hector had an emotional response, even if they were tears of self-pity. It was somehow comforting to know he had it in him, the ability to emote — however indicative it was of his master manipulation. I was happy he cried.

Confronting your enemies, your abusers, is incredibly fraught. You must diminish your expectations, and go into it for yourself only, with no hopes of change or resolution. If you need an apology or admission in order to heal, proceed with caution. But if you strive to be heard, to voice what you've been shouting inside your head for too long, to seek forgiveness on your own terms, then the process can be profound on your path to healing.

Valentina's final break of true freedom from Abuelito Hector would come years later.

25

Over the nine years after Valentina and I confronted Abuelito Hector, our immediate family went through the wonders of searching for and finding ourselves continuously — through college, travel, jobs and loves won and lost. I spent months at a time in Mexico, discovering the natural beauty of my country's central states — all the while blasting the soundtrack of the latest Frida Kahlo movie starring one of my all-time favorites, Salma Hayek. And Abuelita Elena passed away at 106 years old.

Abuelita Elena,
Your death was bittersweet. As long as your life was, I still, selfishly, wanted your spirit of wisdom and laughter to never leave. We celebrated you with lots of color and music, honoring the queen you were in most of our lives. We now connect with your energy in a different way, allowing our spirits to be unbound and reach you in the subtle realms beyond conscious reality. Abuelita, the shaman. You harvested seeds of love, helping us plant healthy trees from hearty roots. I love you forever.

I moved around the world and then to San Francisco where I met the person I would plan to spend the rest of my life with. I opened up to psychedelics for mental and spiritual health, and felt my heart expand to a size I never knew it could when my nephew — Valentina's first child — was born.

Throughout the years, each member of our family made their own strides in forgiving Abuelito Hector and Abuelita Carmen. The most beautiful outcome of this effort, however, was our reinforced bond. The family needed each other, and we leaned heavily into our familial relationships, keeping a tight community all the while.

It had been even longer, eighteen years, since my abuelitos fled California. In that time, many of the family's sadness and anger transformed into forgiveness. My mom and her brothers wrestled with the truth for close to two decades, some for longer, but to finally liberate themselves from the power of their father's darkness, they wanted to see their father one last time.

In April of 2014, death was hovering over Hector, its henchman debating whether to take him now or come back another time, as it shall come to take us all one day. Esperanza and her brothers planned a visit to Purepero in hopes of telling their father they forgave him before he passed. The timing of the trip ended up aligning with the birth of Esperanza's first grandchild, so her brothers went without her and she stayed back for a more celebratory milestone. Becoming an abuelita gave Esperanza a new joy, and holding her first grandchild took her back to when she first held her own three children. All her stress vanished as she gazed at the beautiful baby in her arms.

The men had had their last moments with their father, but by the time summer rolled around, Hector was still alive. So accompanied by Valentina, Esperanza flew to Purepero to say goodbye. Valentina was nervous and scared to see her abuelito, but her gut was pushing her to be there.

The two women arrived at Hector and Carmen's home with their heads held high and a strong sense of conviction. Hector was lying on the couch in the living room, his eyes following his daughter's every move until she stood directly above him.

"The reason I'm here is to let you know I forgive you, Dad. You need to know I forgave you many years ago. I know you're dying, Dad, and I need you to know it's okay to let go. You do not need to stay here suffering any longer. It's time for you to go."

Hector did not dare take his eyes off his daughter. Once she was done speaking, he looked around the room, grabbing glances from Valentina, Carmen, and his additional caretaker, Carlos. His eyes floated back to his granddaughter.

"I feel like you're angry with me. Are you?" Hector asked Valentina.

"Yes, I am," she replied sternly and sassily.

Instead of responding to her, Hector turned back to Esperanza. He paused before surprising the whole room.

"Mija, will you forgive me? Please? Forgive me. Will you?" he pleaded in pain.

"Yes, Apa. I told you I forgive you. I forgave you many years ago. You can go in peace now. It's your time."

Esperanza and her father did most of the talking. Valentina felt her role was to support her mom and so she focused on being present in this uncomfortable and final visit.

The house phone rang and it was Tío Joel calling from California. Part of him wanted to accompany Esperanza in saying goodbye, but seeing his former best friend one last time proved to be too much. Knowing Esperanza was there, he coordinated with her to say his goodbye over the phone. Glad to hear her tío's voice, Esperanza passed the phone to her father.

"Hello?" said Hector.

"Hi, Hector. Listen, I never thought I would forgive you or ever talk to you again, but I am doing this for Esperanza and my daughters. I love Esperanza like she is my own, especially because you could not. I know nobody is perfect. I have also made mistakes, lots of them, but some punishments we must leave to God. God takes care of all, for me at least, and he will take care of giving you what he believes you deserve in the afterlife. You may go. I forgive you. Goodbye."

The two men hung up the phone and Tío Joel felt a rush of peace. While a weak Hector napped, Carmen, Valentina, and Esperanza went upstairs to look at the photos lining the walls. As Carmen pointed, she told stories dear to her heart, reliving memories of when she was a regular part of their lives. One picture brought Esperanza to a sudden halt. Valentina immediately recognized something was wrong. She wondered why a cute picture of her mom and Abuelita Elena in a bathing suit would make her mom react this way.

"What's wrong?" Valentina asked.

"That is the picture my father used to have on his nightstand. That is the original," Esperanza said, her eyes glued to the picture.

Valentina was shocked, having never heard this before. The idea of her abuelito keeping a picture of her mother in a bikini close to him at all times was enraging. When Carmen led them into another room, Valentina stayed behind to "go to the bathroom." Instead, she took the frame off the wall, flipped it around and tried in a hurry to unlatch the old rigid metal pieces that held the back together. It was only right that her mother become the rightful owner of her image again.

But she struggled with the frame. Panic set in that she might not get it out before her mom and abuelita came back around. Determined, she put those worries out of her mind and focused. To her relief, she got it out and into her pocket mere seconds before the two women came back around the corner.

"We should get going," Esperanza told her daughter.

"Yes, we should," replied Valentina with a satisfied smile.

The three generations of women walked back down the stairs to say their final goodbyes, but before Valentina and Esperanza could walk out the door, Hector directed a question at Valentina.

"Mija, will you forgive me?"

Valentina was caught off-guard. She had not considered this possibility, having already resigned herself to a supportive role. The last time her abuelito spoke to her he lied. She weighed her options quietly.

Hector turned to Carlos, "She won't forgive me. I did some bad things and I do not know that I am going to get her forgiveness."

Valentina took only one second more to spring into action. "Abuelito, I'm right here. If you want to talk to me, talk to me."

"Okay. Are you having a hard time forgiving me?" Abuelito Hector asked.

"No." Valentina was surprised by what came out of her mouth. Staring at his powerless body, she realized she had been holding onto this shame and struggle her entire life, and for the first time, it was vanishing. A cool rush of freedom moved throughout her body as she felt the shame and guilt subside. It was all his now, as it should have been all along.

Despite settling herself on the path of forgiveness years ago, she suddenly felt a bigger relief than anything before. Her forgiveness furthered more than she thought possible. She smiled at her abuelito and said her last words to him. "Actually, Abuelito, I feel pretty free right now."

Hector was unsure of how to respond. There was nothing left to say. His time was nearly up on earth and he knew it.

The two women walked out of the house, onward to Abuelita Elena's, Valentina bursting with a sense of rejuvenation. She turned to her mother, "Mami! Look what I got!" and pulled the picture out of her pocket and handed it to Esperanza. "You keep it, burn it, throw it away, do whatever you want with it," Valentina said happily.

Esperanza's eyes lit up, showing her excitement. "Oh my gosh! I cannot believe you took this! I'm so happy!"

They felt restored. Their moment of reckoning may not have gone exactly how they pictured, but the feeling of their mutual support was invaluable. That photo was a symbol of domination and Valentina removed it from the house, relinquishing the control back to her mother. It quickly became a symbol of closure of Esperanza's trauma.

Valentina did not expect to gain as much from this trip as her mother did, but Esperanza knew she would. That is why she invited her daughter along. The two flew back to California together with a sense of true liberation.

Two months later Hector was still alive, but barely. He was in constant discomfort, and would hold his head and shriek, the unpleasantness written on his face. Esperanza and Ricardo happened to be in Purepero visiting family, walking towards Abuelita Elena's house, when Carlos came running out of Carmen and Hector's home.

"Help! Hector fell off the couch and I can't get him back up! I need help! He's too heavy," he shouted in a panic.

Esperanza and Ricardo were not planning on seeing her parents and were caught off guard by his sudden emergency. Ricardo had never even been inside of his in-laws' home in Mexico — by choice — but to his surprise he intuitively walked toward the house offering his help. He knew what he was about to do, and who he was about to help, but assured himself it was the right thing to do. *This is just a body. This is a sick person. This is a human being. I need to help.*

Ricardo always hoped for closure with his father-in-law for all the severe suffering he inflicted on those closest to him, but he could never have predicted how conveniently life would bring that to him. Esperanza went ahead to Abuelita Elena's while Ricardo walked into his in-laws' house with a feeling of doom, his hands shaking. He approached Hector lying on the floor and helped put him back on the couch.

Ricardo saw how different Hector looked from the last time he had seen him. Hector looked at him and tried to get words out, but the discomfort and medication made them impossible to understand. Ricardo wanted desperately to hear what his father-in-law — the source of his indignation — had to say but couldn't. He tried for a few seconds more, straining to make out his words, but gave up. He realized he did not need them. Like my final encounter with Hector, this moment was for Ricardo and Ricardo alone. He did not need Hector to ask for his forgiveness. Ricardo was naturally overcome with it. He told his father-in-law goodbye and walked out the door.

Ricardo entered Abuelita Elena's home, graciousness filling his soul. He could have left the man on the floor to struggle, as Hector had left Esperanza, Valentina, and many others to do their whole lives, but he acted with integrity instead. As he reflected on what just happened, he laughed to himself and savored the waves of forgiveness crashing upon him. He brought his hands together and closed his eyes, laughing and giving thanks to God. Life had come together beautifully to give him the closure he sought, just as it had for his wife and daughters. He, too, was finally free.

The next day, Ricardo and Esperanza made their way back to California, where she immediately told her brothers their father was sure to die any day now. Four days later, on a Thursday night, Esperanza and Ricardo switched off the lights and went to sleep. Before dawn, they were awoken by the phone ringing.

Hector's caretaker delivered the news Esperanza had been waiting to hear for so long. Her father was dead.

Her body went still, but this time with a strong sense of serenity and salvation. A happy tear streamed down her face before she shook Ricardo to tell him the news. Ricardo, half asleep, beamed with a smile on his face, squeezing his wife's hand with love. Esperanza could not shake the peace she felt with her father's death, nor did she care to. This moment was fully hers.

My mom's face softened with this memory, a slight smile cracked on her face. "My dad's death was a relief. I was not sad. It was not a sorrow. He could no longer hurt me. He could no longer physically hurt anybody. Even though in his final years he could barely move, the disturbance of his existence was still there. Fear would shoot through me every time I randomly saw him walking the streets of Purepero. It was awful. Stress would take over my being and I would become sick, my insomnia worsening for long periods after. Knowing he was gone was comforting and alleviating for me and many others. His death was like a new beginning. I was waiting for that day, waiting for his time to come. He never went to prison or to a mental hospital, so all I could do was wait for him to go away completely. Finally, he did."

Tío Leo shared how he felt after receiving the phone call that his father was gone. "I was not sad. What he did is going to affect my sis for the rest of her life. My heart goes out to her, not to my dad. I am not callous, but at the end of the day he was not a good father. I wish he was, because I have a lot of great memories as a kid. But because of what he did, I did not mourn. There are still many monsters in this world. I just hope his death brought my sis some peace."

At the time of Abuelito Hector's death, I was living in San Francisco. My mom shared the news with me over the phone early Friday morning. It was odd to feel so deeply comforted by someone's death.

I hung up and shared the news with my new boyfriend. He offered natural preconditioned sympathies. "I'm so sorry your grandpa died."

I smiled wide and looked up at him, "Oh no! This is great news! He was a horrible man." I felt like shouting it everywhere I went in celebration.

I decided against attending Abuelito Hector's funeral, but quickly regretted not being there for my mom. Instead, while his body laid to rest, I spoke about it like a new beginning to everyone and anyone who would listen, giddy to revel in his passing. The wicked warlock was dead.

Fernando, Esperanza, Leo, and Daniel all flew out to Purepero together that Friday. The siblings were going, out of a sense of duty and obligation, to put their father's soul to rest and sink his dark abyss under the dirt. They wanted to see with their own eyes that he was going deep underground where he would stay forever.

When Esperanza and her brothers arrived at their parents' house, it was around nine o'clock at night and the road was packed with people gathered around a street fire in front of the house. The town's people came to pay their respects to Hector's life — many unaware of his true character — and the ones to lead the burial had just arrived.

Loved ones accompanied Carmen inside the house, and as the four siblings entered, a lane opened up for them to reach their mother. They gave her a hug and turned to see their father's open casket in the middle of the living room. The brothers made their way to the casket, while Esperanza found herself unable to do the same, plopping herself down on the couch. People cycled through with their condolences. By two a.m., the townspeople made their way back to their homes, leaving Carmen and her children alone with the corpse of their enemy.

It is customary in Mexico for the casket to lay open in the house for one night, while an individual stays awake with the body until the burial the next day. Leo and Esperanza decided to take turns throughout the night. While her brother lay asleep on the couch, Esperanza finally walked over to her dad. Standing over his lifeless body, she took several deep breaths, and with each one came a wave of peace stronger than the last. Her fear of him was gone with his soul.

She shook Leo awake for his turn before drifting off to sleep. Leo sat several feet away from the coffin, gazing into the distance as the wooden grandfather clock transported him to a memory a decade earlier when he visited his father in Purepero.

Standing in his parents' sunroom with his father, surrounded by plants, Leo confessed, "Dad, you are a disappointment as a father, and you brought dysfunction on our family. Your relationship with your children will never be the same. You ruined our family as a whole. We as siblings may have stayed close, but the core of our family was destroyed, and it is your fault."

Hector stood in front of his son, listening attentively and nodding his head, repeating, "I know. I know."

Over the years, Leo stopped going to Purepero as he became less interested in engaging with his father. It was no longer a secret what his father did, and he couldn't pretend like things were normal. In Leo's own words, "You can accept that bad things happened, but you do not need to condone them. Denying someone's hideous actions is the same as excusing them, no matter how much you love the person."

Leo could forgive, but never forget. He looked at the coffin and saw just a box with a body. His relationship with his father died long ago. He had already buried the man he once revered.

Morning arrived and Hector's children prepared to usher their father to his final resting place. After the church service, the funeral attendees walked behind the hearse to the cemetery in a silent processional shrouded in black. Once there, the pallbearers pulled out the casket and walked it carefully through the grounds, past crowds of large, religious monuments, and large cement headstones, through slippery mud from the week's rain.

When they reached the gravesite, everyone gathered around while Hector's sons manually lowered him into the earth. Esperanza stood next to her brothers, peering down at the casket descending six feet underground, dirt settling, covering the physical remnants left of their father. The few tears the brothers shed were for the father they thought they had but never did, for their mother's powerlessness, and for themselves. All the while, Esperanza's eyes remained dry.

I asked my mother how it felt to have never received a sincere apology from her father. She sat up tall, "I forgave my dad, and that was enough."

After decades of chaotic despair, ruminating on painful emotions, unpacking a lifetime of agony, she finally concluded that in order to let go, move on, and enjoy the beautiful life she created for herself, she needed to forgive her father. Holding onto bitterness and anger would only make her more bitter and angry.

"When you forgive someone," she affirmed, "that does not mean you are excusing their actions. Some people have said that because I ended my relationship with my father, I did not truly forgive, but that is absolutely not true. You don't have to maintain a relationship with your predator. You have to do what is best for you, not for them. It's simple: If you do not trust someone or feel uncomfortable around them, you do not need to keep them in your life, no matter who they are.

"Remember that," she said looking at me intently. "You forgive for yourself, not for anybody else. I have forgiven my father, but I will never forget what he did to me."

I stared at my mom in admiration. If she was able to forgive her father and move forward in life, what other beautiful things was she capable of? What other marvelous things are humans who have suffered the worst of atrocities capable of? I felt proud to call her my mom and so, wanting to follow her noble lead, I grabbed the strength of her forgiveness and tucked it into the pocket of my soul.

26

Abuelita Carmen Part I

Throughout the interview process for this book, many of the people I spoke with — as horrified as they were by Abuelito Hector — had a lot to say about Abuelita Carmen. They harbored both deep anger and sincere sympathy for her. In many views, she was of sound mind and the one best positioned to stop the abuse, yet she did nothing. She was complicit in allowing her husband to horrendously abuse her own children and others. When the silence broke, her relationships became irreparable.

My sister's voice sounded with authority and passion from the RV, in an almost poetic rhythm. "Abuelita was a mother figure from the time she was a teenager. That is an incredible amount of responsibility."

My sister dug through our abuelita's history to try and comprehend her ways. "Her mom died when she was young, and she had to take care of and be the role model for her siblings. On top of that, she never went to school past second grade. Not only was she emotionally stunted, she was not educated. All she knew was that she was Mexican and Catholic, and in Mexican and most Latin cultures, if you marry somebody, you stay with them. Divorce is not an option. Back then, women were much more oppressed than they are today. You stuck to your man, you went to church, you were pigeonholed into a role at home, and you raised your children. She was dealt a wild card in life — a pedophile for a husband — and she found out too late in her mind: after starting a life with him and giving birth to a daughter."

Even though my sister and others tried understanding Abuelita Carmen, there was a strong sense of irritation about her unhealthy love for money. She would tell my mom that a man was an excellent husband if and only if he was a reliable provider. This was what she valued most in a man.

She cared about having the biggest house, the best clothes, and the most expensive jewelry.

To this day, the same thoughts and questions linger in the back of people's minds.

Did she allow Hector to do what he did because of the money? Was she simply afraid of losing all her nice things? Or was her obsession with money her escape from a tortured life with the man she loved most in this world?

Without a doubt she was a victim of women's oppression in the 1940s. She was also an immigrant without a clear understanding of this new world — the United States — or the ability to communicate in its native language: English. She likely felt trapped, like she had no choice but to stay.

Many believe Abuelito Hector bought her silence — an unspoken accord that *if you stay quiet and let me sexually molest little girls, you can have anything you want and live like a queen.*

Tío Joel and Tía Victoria wondered if Abuelito Hector could have been cured by spending time in a psychiatric hospital to specifically treat pedophilia. I had never considered this, and even in their sharing, I doubted the possibility of my abuelito's redemption.

While perceptions of Abuelita Carmen varied, most believed she was abused and manipulated by Abuelito Hector, as well, in ways we will never fully understand, nor will she. I believe she was not only mentally and physically abused, but very likely sexually abused, afraid of the consequences if she said no. Over time, much of the family forgave her, and she began visiting the family in California after Abuelito Hector's death. Many, however, never truly felt comfortable in her presence. It required the constant toeing of a thin line between delight, resentment, and heartache.

With Abuelito Hector gone, my mom slowly rekindled a relationship with her mother. After 15 years without speaking, my mom now felt a responsibility for her mother. It was not a sudden shift, rather a gradual one on her quest to peace. It was evident her mother continued living between two distinct realities: one where Abuelito Hector was the best thing that ever happened to her, grieving for him endlessly, and another where she knew exactly how abhorrent her husband was.

"Sometimes it feels like my mom is a stranger," my mom once expressed. "Knowing what was going to happen, she would send me to the wolf anyway, and all of that comes rushing back to me when she visits, so it's hard. She chose to do wrong. Tío Joel and Tía Victoria are my mother and father figure, and I have all the patience in the world for them. I would do anything for them. It does not feel the same with my mom."

Still, both my mom and dad saw her humanity and could not abandon her. My parents' willingness to care for and forgive Abuelita Carmen is an example of the bedrock of love our family thrives on. Listening to each of my family members reflect on their personal hurt and happiness helped me process my own feelings. Being surrounded by such resilience, especially in the face of the greatest adversity, gave me an astounding sense of gratitude. I could hear my mom's and dad's voices merging as they spoke of Abuelita Carmen with similar compassion — evidence of their shared journey. Even through the catastrophes, love remained my parents' centering force.

Abuelita Carmen's response when she first found out what her husband was doing is beyond most people's grasp. Most parents would suffer immense psychological torment if they knew their child was being molested, let alone consistently for years. What happened to Abuelita Carmen? Why did she defend the perpetrator and not the innocent children abused? Our family deserved real answers, especially my mom. My dad's words echoed in my head: *"If you do not know why you did something wrong, then search for the truth."*

I needed to confront my abuelita. I needed to search for Abuelita Carmen's truth if she wasn't going to do it herself.

Abuelita Carmen Part II

I spent months mentally preparing myself to speak with Abuelita Carmen about her role in this story. I was going to show up at her door in Mexico, like any normal visit, but with the sole intent of firing questions at her without giving her a chance to deflect. My mom and I were not sure she would agree to discuss this topic, so I was ready to do whatever it took to get her to open up to me — beg, cry, or intimidate.

In February of 2019, Abuelita Carmen traveled to Southern California for a visit, and I flew back to SoCal — instead of Mexico — to finalize my last interview with her. She stayed with my parents, and on a day only my mom and I were in the house with her, I joined her unassumingly in the family room. My mom fixed herself on the stairs to listen in on our conversation. Abuelita Carmen had no clue what she was in for.

It dawned on me that I was partly talking to my abuelita for my mom. I was going to try and get answers to questions my mom had tried pulling out of her many times. Suddenly, I felt dizzy. I envisioned my mom as a nervous little girl on the stairs, and I as her older sister, fighting for her and all the other children Abuelita Carmen was not able to stand up for.

I took my seat on the couch next to Abuelita Carmen, feeling love and some tribulation. The annoyance was strange for me to feel with her. We talked about life in general and I could hear the nervousness in my voice and feel my heart pounding in my chest. I started talking fast and laughing at comments that were really not that funny. I was trying and failing to sink into the conversation, looking for the right time to ask her to have the conversation with me.

Finally, I blurted out, "Abuelita, I would like to ask you some questions about all the sexual abuse in the family, and Abuelito Hector." She gave me a perturbed look and told me she was not feeling well. My body revved up with anger and a sense of entitlement for the conversation. Water slowly filled my eyes, but not a single tear dropped. I was always sweet with her, so the sharpness in my tone caught us both off guard when I shot back, "You owe me this conversation. You owe it to the family." With that, she nodded her head and I turned on my recorder.

She did not want to have the conversation. She was not ready for it. But the time had come, and she knew.

"How was your relationship with Abuelito when you were first married?" I asked.

"Good, mija." She paused for a bit before looking up, "But... everything begins to end. Everything good eventually goes away. That is the way life is. From the day we are born."

I did not agree with her statement, but could not deny her experience in life.

"How was Abuelito when his father passed away? I know his father was abusive with him," I stated.

"He felt it a whole lot. It's tough to lose one's parents. As good or bad as they are, it is still hard. They are your parents, and they will be your parents until death," she offered.

"Did you ever notice that Abuelito liked little girls before you had kids?" It was unpleasant to put the thought to words. My eyes instantly welled up.

"You know what, mija? I never noticed. I do not know why," Abuelita Carmen said in a low, sad whisper.

"Was Abuelito ever rough with you? Did he ever hit you or talk to you in destructive ways?" I inquired.

"No. Yes. Aaaah, I don't know. He would not get riled up with me," she said contradicting herself.

I could sense her mentally battling which reality to live in. I pushed forward, knowing I didn't have much time. "Do you remember when you first realized he was touching my mom?" I asked nervously.

"Yes. It was when she was three. I took all of his clothes and put them into a suitcase for him, put it outside on the porch and told him to leave, but he would not." Her tone was a sad one, and her eyes showed the memory's grief.

I was shocked, as was my mom. This was the first time we learned Abuelita Carmen tried to get him out of their lives, even if it was a paltry attempt.

"How did Abuelito react when you told him to leave?" I asked.

"He simply said he was not going to. He grabbed the suitcase, walked back inside, and told me, 'The kids need their father. I am not going anywhere.' We argued and I told him several times I wanted him to leave, but he wouldn't have it." She said this with authority, the way he must have said it to her.

"How did it feel? When you first realized your husband was inappropriately touching your daughter?" I could not believe I was getting her to talk.

Without hesitation, Abuelita Carmen admitted, "I felt bad and I reacted badly. It was hard! Extremely hard." She scrunched her eyebrows, closed her eyes, and took a deep breath, letting out sounds of agony.

"Did your relationship with Abuelito change afterwards?"

"We fought a lot, mija." She released more sounds of displeasure, and it became clear that her decision to stay with him instead of helping her own daughter had traumatized her gravely.

"Can you tell me about other times you confronted him?" I was hoping to hear more stories like this.

"No. That was the only time."

My chest tightened, causing my heart to pulse with pain, and I dug my nails into the side of my thighs to keep myself from crying. To my surprise, she kept talking.

"At that point, we were fighting regularly. Women were not the way they are today. That counts for a lot, mija. It was a lot harder back then."

"Maybe it was different for you because you started dating Abuelito at sixteen and married at nineteen. You were with him your whole life." I could hear myself excusing her actions, but really, I was listing the reasons that helped me understand them. I was bothered by my own tendency to do this, and struggled with accepting this list as a form of understanding.

Abuelita Carmen persisted, "It was a lot harder, mija. In those times, one got married much younger. Women nowadays are able to get ahead."

It was true, the world changed drastically for women in her lifetime. Just a few decades prior, she did not have much of a voice as a female. The Catholic church had a tight grip on social norms, deeming divorce a non-option and the role of women domestic and submissive. These elements made it tough for a woman to break away and speak out against any kind of abuse, let alone sexual abuse.

"Did your feelings of love towards him change after you first found out?" I asked.

"Yes, my feelings changed a bit. You can no longer feel the same. I still loved him, but I felt really bad inside."

"Did you and Abuelito ever discuss it in the sense that maybe he was mentally sick, or..."

"No. We did not talk about it at all," she said, cutting me off.

The dam holding back my tears was about to break. "Did you ever tell anybody?"

Her tone never broke from sadness. "Nobody. I never told anybody."

"Why not?" I asked, grieving from the depths of my soul.

"I was stupid and embarrassed," she shrugged her shoulders and it struck me: embarrassment and shame are deeply connected with abuse — not only for survivors, but anyone close to the predator or situation, too. I was slammed with a wave of ignorance never having thought of this before — that she too would feel deep shame. How was it that I could be encircled with sexual abuse and never have thought of this before? Shame and guilt are vicious circles. This was the first time I heard her admit that she handled it poorly, and that she was wrong.

"The sexual and physical abuse that Abuelito Hector inflicted on my mom and Tío Daniel was happening for a long time. What were you thinking during that time? What happened to you that you did not protect them? What happened inside of you?" The dam broke, tears streamed down my face, and yet I stayed composed, intent on asking the questions that needed answers.

She stared out into the space in front of her, her eyes swelling with heartache. She responded with a shaky voice, "Aaaayyyyy, mija. I don't even know what I was thinking." We quietly focused on her heavy short breaths of grief until she spoke again. "The good thing is, it is all in the past now. It already happened and it's in the past," she said, hoping to convince herself she could put it all behind her.

"It happened, but the reality is it continues to affect many of us," I declared, making sure she knew what was done was not done. "It affects people mentally and morphs into physical pain. There is a bright side. It gets better with every generation who speaks up. The truth will set you free." I carried on with my questioning, "How did you find out my mom and your nieces went to the police? And how did the decision to flee come up?"

"I was not at the house when your abuelito first found out about the police report, I was at the spa. When I got home, I knew something big was happening. He immediately said, 'Carmen, we need to leave for Mexico because my mom is getting older and we need to take care of her. I am telling you so you can start packing *now*. We are going to leave this evening.' I started packing right away."

"Did you ask why you needed to leave so suddenly?" I pushed on.

"No, not in that moment." She said this with such conviction, but I was not convinced. I did not believe she wouldn't question the abrupt need to leave her entire family and life to take care of her mother-in-law. She either blocked out crucial details or refused to admit them.

"How did Abuelito find out about the family going to the police?" I pressed.

"I don't know, mija."

I fixated on her every move, trying to decipher her facial expressions and body language to determine if she was lying or had actually convinced herself of alternate endings. I reminded her of the phone call she made to her brother, Joel, asking him to speak to his daughters about rescinding the police report. Her eyes widened as memories buried deep in her subconscious started flooding to the surface.

"Oooooh, yes. I remember..." She trailed off, grunting with discomfort.

Glaring at Abuelita Carmen, I alternated between feelings of indignation and compassion, watching her face reveal the horror and incredulity of her own past, her own actions, lost in her own dark void. I imagined her far down in a black hole, wandering the darkness in fear and self-loathing.

"What were those days in hiding like, before you were able to leave the U.S.?" I asked.

"They were fine. Nobody said anything to us about anything," she assured.

"What was your relationship like with Abuelito during this time?"

"It was good, mija."

It was hard to tell how deliberate her rampant suppression was. I barreled ahead.

"Do you remember when your children went to Purepero to confront you and Abuelito in front of Abuelita Elena?"

"Yes. How could I not?" she said in a low whisper. "I remember listening to my kids and feeling horrible. I do not remember much besides that, or what exactly was said, but I know people spoke the truth that day."

"When my mom talked to you about this during your trip out here for Valentina's quinceañera, why did you stay quiet?"

"Well, because of everything that was happening. Why else?" She was vague.

"What do you mean by 'everything that was happening'?" I pressed her.

"Well, everything that happened." Breathing heavily, she searched for her thoughts before continuing, "One does not want to remember everything that happened. These are terrible memories. You simply do not want to remember," she said in a mournful tone. I was beginning to catch on to just how deliberate her memory suppression was.

"But you are her mother. You should have answered her questions honestly. You were not the only one who was hurt, Abue — "I know!" she cut me off to make sure I knew she understood. "It hurt the entire family, all my kids and grandkids, and others." The mood in the room turned somber before I started up again.

"It's nice to experience that with every generation, the more we talk, the more we heal. Especially by talking about it with one another. Knowing the story helps us to…"

"Heal. To heal." She finished my sentence with an elevated sense of awareness, in a low, calm, yet heartbroken tone.

"Did you ever try and change Abuelito from his pedophilic ways?"

"Yes! Of course, but it's difficult, mija. It is difficult," she said, straining her voice.

"What was the hardest part for you?"

"Separating from my kids. That was the saddest part." She began to cry for the first time during our conversation.

"Why did you decide to flee with Abuelito instead of staying with your kids and grandkids?"

"Because I loved him, mija. I loved him," she said remorsefully.

"Mmmmmm." It was the only response I could manage, realizing she loved him deeply, despite his rotting darkness. She was taught to be loyal to her man, regardless of his actions. These were powerful chains to break, and the only way they would was if Abuelita Carmen shattered her own perceptions. I was not sure this would ever happen. Breaking these chains was an effort my mom's generation began, and one my generation would continue. There was more work to be done, and I was trying.

Nervous my abuelita was losing steam, and may surrender at any minute, I pushed through.

"Did you consider him to be a good husband?"

"Yes," she said, demanding it to be true.

"Yes?" I asked, shocked by her answer.

"Yes," she said softly, with less confidence. "Because he never withheld money, and never told me not to spend it. He did not even know how much we had in the bank. Only I did."

Abuelito Hector was a master manipulator, and never once did I doubt he understood this weakness of hers. By giving her everything she wanted and a false sense of control, he could continue satisfying his darkest compulsions. She was admitting her diseased relationship with money, whether or not she realized it. For her, much of his value as a husband was determined solely by the freedom with which she could spend their money.

It was disconcerting to listen to her, and yet I pitied her so, staring at the invisible cage she built around herself.

"Did you consider him to be a good father?" I asked, concerned with how she might respond. My stomach and throat twisted into knots waiting for her answer.

"Yes, mija. Yes."

My jaw dropped and I stared at her completely astonished. My eyes widened, blinking hard several times and slightly shaking my head. "Even after you found out what he was doing to your only daughter? And your youngest son?" I asked, almost shouting, begging for a better answer.

"It could never be the same." She took several more breaths. "Everything changes. Everything changes a lot, mija," she said unhappily.

Her response deeply irritated me. When she was not looking, I rolled my eyes out of frustration and confusion. I did not have the energy to push her further on this, so I moved on.

"Were you ever jealous of my mom and the sexual attention Abuelito gave her?" I immediately felt uncomfortable but was forced to sit with it.

"Noooooo. Nothing like that. No." She chuckled and smiled, as if it were absurd, but nothing was out of the question in this story. Her face turned back into a frown.

"How did you feel when Abuelito passed away?"

She threw her hands up and in a bleak tone exclaimed, "Ooooh, I always ask God why he did not take me instead, because the one who stays, stays to suffer, and the one who goes, is gone." She shrugged her shoulders and allowed a period of mourning. Her body hurt and she let out a sharp little "Ay ay ay." She had, after all, been carrying around an enormous amount of heavy trauma most of her life.

I was working my way down a list of questions in front of me and had reached one of the most anticipated of all.

"If you could do it all over again, would you make the same choice and flee with him, or would you stay with your children?" I held my breath.

"I would go with your abuelito," she said quite honestly. And though it took my breath away, I quickly recovered. I had to.

"So, if you were given the chance to do it all over again, you would make the same choices and stay with him?" I asked again, feeling like she could not have properly understood my question.

"Yes," she declared again, matter-of-factly. She had understood my question the first time around. I tensed up.

"And you would leave your children, again?" I pushed the hot button.

"Ayyy, well who knows, mija. That is where it gets complicated."

"You loved him that much?" I questioned with doubt and disappointment written all over my face.

"Yes."

I thought of my mom on the stairs, hearing answers she did not want to hear. Abuelita Carmen's whole identity was defined by her relationship with Abuelito Hector and it made her lose track of herself, and of a healthy, honest life. Walking unlit paths, she came to a split in the road many times, repeatedly following her husband's steps to pure destruction, out of fear and oppression. I — and I am sure others — have wondered what Abuelita Carmen's life would have been like if she had fallen in love and married a different man. A normal man. Not a violent pedophile.

Carmen Flores Montel's dream in life was to be a mother, a grand host, an excellent cook, and watch her grandchildren grow. While some of those dreams may have come true, what good were they to her standing on quicksand? Her own fears robbed her of her life's dreams.

She never did get to watch her grandchildren grow, and I wanted her to recognize the depth of hurt that came from feeling as if she willingly surrendered herself to be kidnapped away from her family. I wanted her to understand without hurting her. So after debating sharing my next thought, which I knew would be unpleasant for her, I remembered my objective: the truth.

"Abuelita, I am not sharing this with you to make you feel bad, but…"

She cut me off, reassuring me whatever I was going to divulge about my feelings would be more than okay.

"When Abuelito passed away, I was really happy. I have never felt sad. Not once." It was a hard statement for her to hear, as she made little grunting noises to release the pressure in her body. She took my hand in hers and nodded her head.

The discussion was wearing her out, and I got the core of what I wanted, so I concluded our conversation.

"What advice would you give someone going through what you went through?"

"I would advise them to separate, and to not be dumb. Having gone through it myself, I would never wish that on another person. So, do not be dumb. Separate. That is it," she said in a wounded voice.

I instantly cried and felt a tinge of freedom with her words. But I was still confused by her conflicting logic to flee with Abuelito Hector if she had a second chance. These situations are many things, but never simple. I followed my breath, making sure to soothe myself with love so as not to lose my way.

"Those are all the questions I have right now, Abuelita."

Her face lit up with relief, allowing the tension to melt and a slight smile to stretch on her face, which made me chuckle. I would be relieved, too.

"Thank you for the conversation," I told her.

"I love you very much, mija," she responded.

"I love you too, Abuelita."

"I love you more, mija." She gave me a kiss on the cheek and embraced me. Then she pulled back to look at me, took my hands in hers, and said: "Mija, God has us here for a reason. There has to be a reason. You use whatever you need to from our conversation in order to help others." She gave me another hug, and I released a storm of tears.

For decades, my family had been seeking these answers, and now, we had them. Abuelita Carmen rested her brittle bones on the couch and closed her eyes to nap. I made my way up the stairs and into my parents' bedroom, where I found my mom slouched on her bed. I collapsed next to her. Yet again, my mom felt her mother's abandonment, confused by her advice to others that she could not follow herself. In the exhaustion and sadness of it all, we found a wild strength. I told my mom she always had me to lean on in life, and she turned to me and smiled. A melody of birds chirping outside the window lulled us to sleep for an afternoon nap.

Abuse, as with many of life's most challenging themes, is complex, its range of colors far exceeding the black and white simplicity most people would prefer. The closed mind prefers a narrow view, but the open mind recognizes the nuance of human thought and emotion. Just like humans, trauma is dynamic, multifaceted, and messy.

My own inner thoughts clashed. Logical opinions of loved ones around me told me to exclude my abuelita from my capacity of love, yet I could not. My love for her would not budge. In fact, I was developing more empathy towards her. Regardless of how much I reflected on her grave mistakes, her neglect of her children and grandchildren, the love endured. I hope my sincere love strengthens her. The role of a grandmother in Latin culture is a significant one, so slowly, a part of me died, only to bloom again.

The light in my family overpowers the dark. When I love her, I feel free, and that is how I know it is right. It allows me to open up a bigger portal of love and forgiveness in the world. My body had been waiting to care for and love these vile pieces of our family history that went unloved for generations.

I was grateful for Abuelita Carmen's honesty, however unsettling her answers were for our family. Somewhere in her lived a desire to help liberate others from a similar plague. Her advice to separate from your abuser, and the permission she granted me to use anything I needed from our conversation, were powerful indications of her desire to evolve. I believe the green light to use what I needed from our conversation was her final gift to our family: the willingness to place herself in the center of the stage, knowing she would likely be devoured.

Abuelita Carmen is an example of what happens when we allow dark to overcome light — a struggle within all of us at different measures. I will take that lesson with me throughout life, allowing her errors to motivate me. For that, I am grateful. For that, I will always love her.

Live in love, in all that you do.
This can be harder than you think.
Darkness is heavy and feels powerful.
Light is weightless and feels like freedom.
We must surrender to the light,
while learning to love the dark.

27

There is a tremendous amount of beauty in life. Catching a leaf falling, spiraling down to the ground, offering a little dance from nature just for us. Watching the clouds create images while they move through the sky, providing waves of calm and serenity. The times we gather with family and friends in laughter, enveloping us in joy. And the feeling of love.

The opening up and honesty surrounding the topic of sexual abuse in our family started slowly, blossoming as my generation grew older. Secrets were no longer permitted, and bravely, one by one, we broke the chains of silence, sharing with one another the experiences we lived, the secrets we kept, and the fear we held. This allowed us to plant new seeds and grow hearty roots in fertile ground. We are no longer rotting roots in the dark abyss, starving for light, though we will never forget that struggle.

My parents have worked extremely hard to overcome their troubles and create a safe space for us to communicate in spite of an incredible amount of family trauma, and I am forever appreciative of that. I am beyond grateful for their endless effort and their continued ability to faithfully give me the two things I need most from our family history: the truth, and the ability to speak about this topic with them to my soul's content.

There are many ways to heal, Esther Perel, a world-renowned psychotherapist, boiled healing down to its essence: "In terms of healing, what we do know is that pain is universal, but the meaning that we give to our pain, and the way we narrate our pain, is highly cultural and contextual. What makes the trauma worse is not the event itself, it's the isolation, the secrecy, and the shame that you have to then live with afterward. And there is nothing that helps us deal better with those experiences than our connections with others. Social connection is the number one salve for most of the pain, and the hurt, and the trauma that we will experience. And communities that come together naturally will provide that kind of buffer."

Our family became that community. It starts at home.

At times I consider my abuelito to be one of the most dangerous men to walk this planet, and yet I would not be here without him. I let that settle into my mind and wonder what that means for the energy within myself. For a second, my heart skips a beat, only to flutter into light and comfort. I know that the beauty of life lies in our control — we can choose to radiate any kind of energy we please into the universe. I choose love. As psychiatrist Bessel van der Kolk states in his book *The Body Keeps the Score*, "Our capacity to destroy one another is matched by our capacity to heal one another."

I used to feel shame, embarrassment, and guilt if I was not angry or harsh enough towards my abuelito. I now understand that these emotions built a cage around me, and I have all the control within to tear the cage down and keep it down. My key to freedom lies in forgiveness.

All of the brave survivors I spoke with brought up feelings of shame, embarrassment, and guilt about what happened to them as children. Unfortunately, these emotions are commonly attached to trauma.

When forced into a situation you're not able to escape or defend yourself from, freezing is a natural response. But it is often matched with deep shame and a sense of disqualification from speaking up. Resist this! The only person who deserves to carry shame, embarrassment, and guilt is the person who inflicted the abuse.

Forgive yourself.

Forgive others.

Shame, embarrassment, and guilt perpetuate silence. Silence is an epidemic in trauma and helps no one, least of all those abused.

Feelings of fear, shock, shame, and guilt are just that: feelings. Emotion is not truth, but emotions need to be felt to be alleviated. The sooner you sit in curiosity with those feelings, march through them, and start talking to people about your experience, the sooner you will tear yourself from the rotting vines of trauma you are ensnared in, leading you closer and closer to psychological, physical, and spiritual freedom.

The individuals abused in this book expressed that their shame was accompanied by a vivid feeling of dirtiness. Non-consensual sex acts with an adult — before you even know what sex is — is a dark, grimy hell. The rotting vines that slithered around my mother, choking her, grew from contaminated soil. These infected vines can overpower you. You've committed no wrong other than falling prey to a force more powerful than you, pulling you into their dark underworld where purity is tarnished. You feel dirty and it lingers with you for a long time.

Neglected emotions put our bodies on constant defense, whether or not we're in the presence of a real threat. Trauma is written into our brain's muscle memory, and we must consciously find new ways for our muscles to react to these memories or else the emotions take on a physical form, spreading through our bodies, taking over corners of our lives we did not know they could, and keeping us in a constant state of mental and physical battle.

In van der Kolk's words from *The Body Keeps the Score*:

"Trauma victims cannot recover until they become familiar with and befriend the sensations in their bodies. Being frightened means that you live in a body that is always on guard. Angry people live in angry bodies. The bodies of child-abuse victims are tense and defensive until they find a way to relax and feel safe. In order to change, people need to become aware of their sensations and the way that their bodies interact with the world around them. Physical self-awareness is the first step in releasing the tyranny of the past... As long as you keep secrets and suppress information, you are fundamentally at war with yourself...The critical issue is allowing yourself to know what you know. That takes an enormous amount of courage."

Overcoming this battle will not be as easy as telling yourself 'Let it go,' but with persistence and the right help, you can overcome it. Van der Kolk also wrote, "...the fact that we can actually change our own physiology and inner equilibrium by means other than drugs is rarely considered." This shows the power we have to be our own healers.

Look at yourself and your life path with love and respect. Know that your past traumas do not define you, rather build character in a puzzle of many other delightful pieces.

Partners play a pivotal role in our healing from trauma. Throughout my life, and especially throughout the writing of this book, I heard responses by partners that both pleased and pained me.

A partner who has been sexually abused needs to hear the words, "It's okay. This doesn't change the way I think of you," and perhaps most notably, "Tell me what happened. I'm here for you." They need their partner to take their own feelings out of the situation and give them the space to talk, not talk, cry, not cry — whatever they want that space for.

A partner who has been sexually abused does not need blame placed on them. Fear has a cruel way of masking itself as anger. Damaging phrases like, "It's your fault," or "You allowed this," make a person shrivel back into themselves, and can get hurled with no regard for consequence. This is a time for healing, not name-calling or guilt-tripping. Waiting potentially years to share their trauma is not a show of disrespect, it is a show of shame that a partner should be compelled to abate. Sharing these experiences is immensely vulnerable and ought not to be met with rage and resentment. Survivors do not deserve these reactions, least of all from their partners.

Men have long been discouraged from emotional expression, and as a society we are only just waking up to this deeply harmful conception of masculinity — and most of the partners of abuse victims are men, although not all.

When you've never been taught how to manage your feelings, and you learn your partner was sexually abused, finding the appropriate way to respond, instead of react, can be a landmine. Breathe. Show love. Show patience. Show interest. If you have already given a negative reaction, apologize and begin laying the groundwork of rebuilding that trust so your partner can share. Being a safe, non-judgmental confidant is one of the most essential pieces of the partner role. When you allow your partner the space to share with you, you can process and evolve together instead of apart.

Above all else, the relationship with oneself is the most influential. Though the sexual abuse in the family was prominent, it was not the lead character in any of our lives — even for my mom. She is alive today because she connected with herself and God, anchoring her spiritual health. She is alive today because she worked hard to focus on her happiness. She was able to bloom out of the tortured life she lived. She learned that to forgive meant to set herself free.

To this day, it is the little joys day to day and the power of her forgiveness that keep her out of the burning jungle of hell her father was doomed to.

"I want people to see that there are many moments to look forward to in life," my mom declared. "There is no map showing how to move past this kind of trauma, but it can be done. You can become a healthy and happy survivor, but you have to look for the good in your life. You have to focus on the positive, no matter how tiny, because if you focus on the negative it is very easy to lose track. For me, forgiving was one of the most influential steps. Remember, forgiving is not forgetting, because I will never forget, but I was able to forgive, and that is my freedom."

My life's fascination with higher consciousness comes not only from trauma — inherited and my own — but even more so from the long line of powerful and resilient relatives and ancestors.

My life has led me down many paths of great surrender, but none of them quite like therapy, plant medicine (best when combined with therapy), and meditation. These three forms of healing connect me to myself, to the world around me, to my most significant relationships, my fears, my weaknesses, my strengths, my joys, allowing me to understand at a level deeper than anything I've experienced, that no matter what happens, the center of my being can never be taken or destroyed because my center is love.

Working out trauma through these methods is to the mind what working with a surgeon is to a diseased heart, or what working with a fitness trainer is to the body. Do not be ashamed to take the steps needed to care for yourself, regardless of stigma. Ignore the mistaken idea that therapy is only for those who suffer from a mental illness or having something "wrong" with them, and that plant medicines are dangerous or ineffective, and that meditation is only for the spiritual.

These negative perceptions come purely from a shallow understanding of what these tools have to offer the human mind, body, and soul. Reaching a higher level of consciousness beyond our daily lives is part of human advancement. It is part of human nature. Expanding our consciousness allows us to connect with our own capabilities as humans and the capabilities of the universe. The value here is we come to understand that all things, including humans, are interconnected and one. Education is key.

Although there is darkness, there is also light. More of it is available to us than we could ever dream of. I am light. You are light. We are light, which means that over the years, myself and others deeply wounded by Abuelito Hector found ourselves basking in loving light, learning to accept, breathe, trust, forgive, and let go.

My maternal abuelitos were a blazing fire in the darkest abyss of our lives, and yet, despite the damages they left marked on each of us, the aftermath of the fire brought with it beautiful new perspectives on how to be in this world. It allowed for us to burn the rotting roots that gripped us for once and for all, creating ashes that gave nutrients to a new ground of soil, with new seeds far above the dark abyss, instead of remaining captive in it for eternity.

Hopefully, through learning about the root causes of our disturbances, we can unlearn destructive thoughts and behaviors, leading us to a state of restoration. Diving deep within ourselves takes time. Be patient with yourself. Only you can choose to dive head first into your own abyss in order to expand your consciousness.

Find a healthy way of tending to your being that works for you and do it often, allowing it to be a catalyst to the realities of the universe around you, above you, below you, beside you, and inside you. It is amazing what humans can endure, coming out of unthinkable suffering with a force of natural strength and determination to lead with love. The pain in our lives can force us to understand that in the end, if we allow it, love — especially self-love — can transform the harshest realities into boundless love.

As I write and edit this last chapter, trying to so eloquently wrap up this story, it is September 1st, 2020. I work from my sky lit home office in Amsterdam, staring at a Buddha figurine on my desk, holding a small ball out in front of him, laughing his big belly laugh. This figurine reminds me that life is at the same time so small and yet so grand. It reminds me to relax and allow life to flow naturally. As Lao Tzu once recognized: Nature does not hurry, yet everything is accomplished.

To my right I see the Virgin Mary in a small silver frame. Her vibrant colors and loving demeanor remind me that I am unconditionally loved. She reminds me that I too have unconditional love inside of me, for myself and all of those around me. It reminds me to tap into this love.

To my left I keep another figurine of a Buddha head with closed eyes and a prominent dot on the third eye. It's been a while since I allowed myself to close my eyes and feel my own third eye. I must admit, I do not give myself enough time to drop into the quietude of myself, no matter my eagerness to do so. Laid directly in front of this Buddha head is an invaluable neon green rosary that my Abuelito Antonio gave to me a couple years before he passed. I hold it in my hands quite often and pass it from one hand to the other while I read and edit. I often speak to my ancestors with this rosary and remember what my Abuelito Antonio once told me: 'You can create hours of images and watch an entire movie in your head alone. What kind of movie you watch is up to you.'

His words bring to mind the importance of mind-body connection. This is not a widely accepted paradigm in most Western societies and therefore, we do not understand the chaos and fear that the broken connection between these two creates. In order to allow for healing, we must hold space for survivors to speak out. This is a key component to healing, because unfortunately, there are many sexual abuse survivors. Sexual abuse is pervasive and does not discriminate against race, gender, religion, or class. No culture is immune.

Mind-body connection is most valuable when grounded in love and understanding, which thrive on empathy. Empathy asks us as a society, to talk to one another, listen closely and relate. Love and understanding do not divide, and we are unfortunately experiencing a high level of division in our societies today. We must tap into our own love and affinity and talk about sexuality, boundaries, consent, and abuse — regardless of religion. I hope this book shows the power these conversations can have on a person's passage to liberation.

People often question why my mom and others stayed silent for so long about what my abuelito did to them. Without the empirical understanding of lived trauma, particularly childhood abuse, it's hard to imagine the true weight of pain and fear that can reduce your voice to nothing. But it's not impossible. Try it. Empathy is our greatest hope for a culture of justice.

It may seem unfathomable to some, but I feel empathy for my Abuelito Hector. It was not always like this, I assure you. There were years I was filled with maddening rage towards him. I held unbearable pain and sadness imagining what could have caused my abuelito to do the things he did, showing itself all throughout my journals with "perfectly daggered statements" made up of mainly curse words.

And just the other day, as I sat at my desk editing chapter 25, I began to bawl, and I realized I had not yet fully forgiven my abuelito. All this time, all this interviewing, all this writing, was to bring me to that moment where I cried myself to the realization that I had never said the words out loud and never truly felt them. On that day I smiled, and even now the tears fall with a smile on my face, as I hear myself say: Abuelito, I forgive you. I forgive you.

And I know that for the first time, I mean these words I say aloud. I release him, and with that, I release myself. I abandon the fear of not being angry at a person logic tells me I should be angry at. And I understand, just a little more, the meaning of unconditional love for the self.

My mom and I gathered in the dining room for what would be our last recording. The house was bright, and the warmth of the sun coming through the windows.

"Did you want to do a meditation or prayer before this?" I asked my mom.

"A prayer would be nice. I prayed before you got here," she replied.

"Yeah. I did a short little meditation too," I said smiling.

My mom started laughing and we got comfortable and grabbed each other's hands. She led us in a prayer.

"God, we ask you to guide us as we continue with the book, the writing of my life. Please be present in the writing and in my memories. Give us strength and knowledge we need for this book." She looked up at me, "Would you like to add anything, Amelia?"

"Sure," I said smiling. "Dear Universe and Dear Self, please be with us throughout the course of this journey. Be present in our minds and souls so that we may lean on your everlasting energy and wisdom. Wrap a white light of protection around us so we may transform beautifully and process the negative emotions into light. Allow this book to be with us in a positive manner. Fill us with love while we work through this."

"Amen." We said in unison, smiling at each other. This was the first time my mom ever shared her story in so much detail with anyone.

And so to all of those who have been abused and have risen back — or are on the rise — we extend our hearts to you and send you love. You are our heroes.

"The struggle of life is one of our greatest blessings. It makes us patient, sensitive, and God like. It teaches us that although the world is full of suffering, it is also full of the overcoming of it." - Helen Keller

BONUS READ

ADVICE

I asked those I interviewed to give their advice to readers finding themselves in similar situations. Everyone's words and hopes are powerful reflections of what they wish they would have done in the past. Take this and use it for your present.

My dad: "I hope this book helps people become aware of a problem — if it exists — and have a more educated perspective than I did. Try your hardest to make sure you are not part of a cycle that repeats itself. Don't be so naive. Understand that you need to cope with the issues at hand. One of the most powerful ways to do this is by talking about the abuse. Talk about it with your partner. Be involved in the conversation. This is an inevitable part of coping and healing.

I wish I had talked about it a lot more with your mom back then. When I talk about it now, I hear others' thoughts that help bring meaning and peace. This world is full of sexual abuse unfortunately, but keeping it hidden is the worst thing one can do. Silence takes you to places you do not want to be. It is better to get it out of your system, one way or another, and I think the best way is by talking."

My sister: "When I experienced bad things, I was able to see the good as very good and become deeply grateful. Throughout my life, my parents continuously showed me that love prevails. If you're not in that space, remember that life is a journey and you're where you are meant to be. One day at a time. Feel the sun, dance, and when in doubt… choose love."

Tía Elsa: "You have to talk about it. Especially when you feel like you can't. It is far from easy, but it is the best medicine. You don't feel dirty anymore. You feel clean. The more you talk about it, the more you come to find out you are not alone."

Michelle: "To all the adults: talk to your kids about sexual abuse. I have a feeling the MeToo movement will help with this, but it may never stop, so talk to your kids constantly."

April: "Be brave. Be strong. Speak up."

Tía Emma: "From my point of view, being open and honest makes a tremendous amount of difference. Decisions can only be made based on information you have. Secrets always seem to blow up, so communicate. Whether abused or not, giving yourself grace to know it is not your fault is huge. Be kind to yourself. Try not to think that in sharing, others will think badly of you. You do not have to fix anything but talking about it will bring the truth out into the open, and in the long run that can only help."

Tío Leo: "To the ones who live with those who were hurt, just love them, for whatever their quirks may be, it is not their fault. Whatever imperfections you think they have, those were instilled by some pretty tragic events, so just love them for who they are. Accept all the positives and accept the quirks and negatives. Whether ten people read this book or ten thousand, I don't think it matters, as long as it brings comfort to those it affected, I am all for it. Again, whatever my sis wants. Let more healing begin!"

ACKNOWLEDGMENTS

To my mom and dad, you are the pillars of my life.

To my sister and brother, my strength throughout life has largely come from you. Two of my greatest inspirations, keeping each other grounded, and supporting each other unconditionally. I am beyond grateful we share an unbreakable bond as siblings, best friends, walking together in this life. I owe much of my happiness and sanity growing up to the two of you. I love you beyond anything I will ever be able to express.

To my partner, thank you for supporting and challenging me along this writing process. You are a strong and resilient soul. I sit back and watch you often with amazement. You are my favorite place to be.

Cassiel Archdeacon, this book simply could not have been written without you. You are the hidden savior of every sentence in this book.

Hugo Rivera, the beautiful artwork on the cover of this book is owed to your generosity, your heart, and your talent.

To my first group of readers, Aunt Wendy, Rachael, Lorraine, Linda, Samantha, Sara — you were all invaluable in shaping this book for the world.

To Maya, and all the therapists supporting people in trauma, thank you. I am immensely grateful for the work you do. You support vital steps for humans along their course of healing. In your own ways, you help stop trauma and push forward the strong spirit of generations of women and men. You helped save my mom from herself, and for that, I will forever be grateful.

CPSIA information can be obtained
at www.ICGtesting.com
Printed in the USA
BVHW072248230521
607980BV00002B/58

9 781735 026800